Spring Harvest

Praise 2006/07

Enclosed in this songbook is a CD ROM with a range of resources which include:

• 2006 Songbook Resources

- • OHP Masters and Text Files of songwords
- • Access to PDF of Lyrics with Guitar Chords
- • OHP Masters and Text Files of Liturgy & Prayers
- • Clear copyright information

• Other Spring Harvest Resources

• NOOMA

Short films on DVD between 10 – 15 minutes long with a 32 page discussion book. For group settings, congregational meetings or personal reflection.

• Words of Worship Demonstration

A song-word projection software for use in your local church with an advanced song search system for smooth distraction-free worship.

Copyright and photocopying

Acknowledgements

Scripture quotations taken from the HOLY BIBLE, NEW INTERNATIONAL VERSION.
Copyright © 1973, 1978, 1984 by International Bible Society. Used by permission of Hodder and Stoughton Limited. All rights reserved. "NIV" is a registered trade mark of International Bible Society. UK trademark number 1448790

Music type setting and new arrangements by David Ball, davidoxon@aol.com
Cover design by Adept Design
Printed in England by Halcyon

Published by Spring Harvest, 14 Horsted Square, Uckfield, East Sussex, TN22 1QG, UK.
Spring Harvest. A Registered Charity.
Distributed by ICC, Silverdale Road, Eastbourne, East Sussex, BN20 7AB, UK.

Spring Harvest wishes to acknowledge and thank the following people for their help in the compilation and production of this songbook: David Clifton, Andrew Crookall, Mel Holden, Cheryl Jenkinson, Geraldine Latty, Phil Loose, Andrew Maries, David Peacock, Sue Rinaldi, Tre Sheppard and Spring Harvest Head Office staff.
Thank you to Marie Birkinshaw, Fiona Jo Clark, Mark Earey, Andy Flannagan, Anne Harrison, Nick Harding, Graham Kendrick, Martin Leckebusch, Northumbria Community, Chris Porteous, Sue Rinaldi, Ruth Sermon, Joy and Lydia Townhill, Pat Turner and Chris Wright for liturgy and worship tips.

ISBN 1 899 78855 7

Contents

Songs are listed in order of first line, not title. In a few cases, alphabetical ordering of songs has been changed slightly, in order to ensure that page turns are not needed in any two-page songs.

The words edition of this songbook is also available in Braille and Giant print

Index

Song titles differing from first lines are in italics

4

All around your throne

Sue Rinaldi

1. All a-round your throne there are an-gels sing-ing,
2. All a-round your throne there are prai-ses ris-ing,
3. All a-round your throne ho-ly ground is burn-ing,

all a-round your world there are voi-ces sing-ing.
all a-round your world men and wo-men ris-ing, sing-ing
all a-round your world there is faith re-

Ho-ly,— ho-ly,— ho-ly is— the Lord.—— Ho-ly,—

ho-ly,— ho-ly is— the Lord.——

1a   Worship the Creator

In a changing world where climatic variations and nature
bring new springs, and uncertain surprises
as we wake to welcome or to draw to a close each day,
so let us recognise you the Creator of the bird song
and by the movement of the sun
may your love dawn in our hearts
as we rise to worship you NOW.
Fill us with your peace and with the beauty
of your complete and unfailing forgiveness.
Now and for ever, **Amen.**

All creation cries to you
(God is great)

Capo 2(A)
Strongly

Marty Sampson

1. All cre-a-tion cries to you, worship-ping in spi-rit and in truth.
2. All cre-a-tion gives you praise, you a-lone are tru-ly great,
3. All to you, O God we bring. Je-sus teach us how to live.

Glo-ry to the Faith-ful One, Jesus Christ, God's Son.
you a-lone are God who reigns for e-ter-ni-ty.
Let your fi-re burn in us that all may hear, and all may see.

This song is recorded on the double album *Celebrating 25 Years of Spring Harvest*

God is great, and his praise fills the earth,—

fills the hea - vens, and your name will— be praised—

— through all— the world._____ God is great, sing his

praise all the earth,—— all the hea - vens, 'cause we're

liv - ing for— the glo - ry of— your name,_____ the

(continued over...)

2a God of our lives

God who made us and made all creation,
God who died for us lives for us,
God who gives us strength and gives us power
God Three in One, be with us now and all our days. **Amen.**

All creation is a song
(Creation's King)

Paul Baloche
& Graham Kendrick

glo - ry, pow - er   to Cre-a-tion's King.___   Songs of earth___ and

songs of hea - ven   join as one to bring,___   bless-ing, ho - nour,

glo - ry, pow - er   to Cre-a-tion's King.___

4

As the light of the sun
(Lord of the harvest)

Words: Andy Bromley & Chris Bowater
Music: Andy Bromley

As the light of the sun— in the earth,— let sal-va-tion be known.—

As the wa-ters co-ver the sea,— let your glo-ry fill— the earth.—

——— E-v'ry tribe,— e-v'ry tongue,— e-v'ry peo-

ple on— the earth— would hear of your fame, hear the sound of your name.—

Lord of the har-vest, send out the wor-kers,

This song is recorded on the Spring Harvest New Songs 'Sing' album

5

Astounded by the mystery
(Majesty)

Paul Oakley

Majesty, I'm on my knees, I'm bowing down before your throne. Jesus, this is your world, you're reigning now, let your kingdom come, your love made known.

Your glory fills the earth, great is our God.

(continued over...)

Making songs work

'It was wonderful at Spring Harvest…but it doesn't quite sound the same when we do it'.

Familiar words from many a worship team leader after introducing a brand new top tune into their church community. Post-meeting analysis concludes that without 5,000 people singing and a 10 piece music band playing, assisted by great sound amplification saturating an atmospheric marquee, the song may need a bit of a re-think to make it work in their home church comprising of 100 people and a band of four using sound equipment that Noah passed on.

Whenever we hear a song on CD or experience it live at a big event, it is always good to go though the process of contextualising it into your own situation. Creativity and flexibility are important elements in this process.

Music teams vary in sound dynamic and structure from church to church and from region to region. Each have different strengths, different characteristics and different cultural identities, and this creativity of sound and configuration is wonderful. When rehearsing a new song with your music team, allow it to be coloured by your own distinctive blend of creativity and character and you will find that the song breathes more easily and sounds more authentic.

Try also to have a flexible approach to the song. You may need to substitute the rock-out guitar solo you first heard for a saxophone moment because you simply do not have a rock out guitarist to hand! Or you may need to arrange the song more acoustically because you do not have a drummer. You may also need to change the key to make it more suitable for the female song leader.

To help make this transition a little easier, Spring Harvest's 2006 New Songs CD *'Our God Reigns'* is a double album and CD 2 presents the big songs in a style more accessible to small bands and smaller gatherings, featuring arrangements for a worship environment where drums, bass and solo instruments are not always available. This songbook contains copies of all the songs on the *'Our God Reigns'* CD.

Also remember that even though the song holds associated memories for you of a sacred moment from night 3 or a glorious awakening from day 4, most people in your congregation will not possess that same immediate affiliation to the song. Make room for a fresh response and place the song within an appropriate flow which will enable worshippers to worship in spirit and in truth.

Sue Rinaldi
www.soundhouse.uk.com : www.homepage.mac.com/suerinaldimedia

6

Astounding grace

With conviction

Words: D.A. Carson
Music: Steve James & Philip Percival

Verse   Em   Bm7+4

1. A - stound - ing grace,   that   God   the   Son   should choose
2. The word made flesh,   the   Son   of   God   a   man,
3. A - stound - ing grace,   that   we   should en - ter in;
4. A - stound - ing grace,   that   Christ should suf - fer death,

Em   C   D2   Em

to leave the Fa - ther's glo - ry, and re - fuse   to clutch his dig - ni-
the time - less one clothed in   a mor - tal span. Now born of dust, and
he tore the veil, and cast a - way our sin;   he saw our hate, our
and know first-hand the grave's cor-rupt-ing breath, the Prince of life, cre-

Bm7+4   Em   C   Dsus4 D

ty, ex - ploit his right   and make him - self a no - one in our sight.
in a man - ger laid: tran - scen-dent God in hu - man like-ness made.
dark and de - sp'rate lust;   he bore our guilt, and then de - clared us just.
a - tion's gra - cious Lord: he paid the price that we could not af - ford.

Chorus   G   D   Am   C   G   D

All praise   Christ and his a - stound-ing grace,   all praise___ his___

6a   Prayer of St Richard

Thanks be to you, our Lord Jesus Christ,
for all the benefits which you have given us,
for all the pains and insults which you have borne for us.
Most merciful Redeemer, Friend and Brother,
may we know you more clearly,
love you more dearly,
and follow you more nearly, day by day. **Amen.**

Prayer of St Richard

Beneath the cross of Jesus
(Beneath the cross)

7

Keith and Kristyn Getty

Gently & thoughtfully

1. Be - neath the cross of Je - sus, I__ find a place to stand; and__ won - der at such mer - cy that__ calls me as I am. For__ hands that should dis - card me, hold__ wounds which tell me 'come'. Be - neath the cross of Je - sus my un -

neath the cross of Je - sus his__ fam - ily is my own. Once__ stran - gers chas - ing self - ish__ dreams, now__ one through grace a - lone. How__ could I now dis - ho - nour the__ ones that you have loved? Be - neath the cross of Je - sus see the

neath the cross of Je - sus, the__ path be - fore the crown, we__ fol - low in his foot - steps where__ pro - mised hope is found. How__ great the joy be - fore us – to__ be his per - fect bride. Be - neath the cross of Je - sus we will

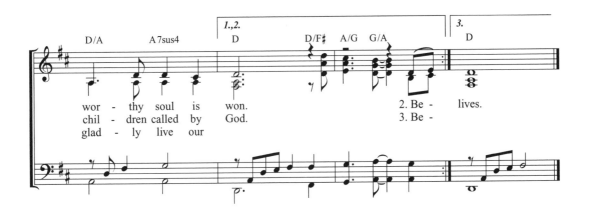

wor - thy soul is won.
chil - dren called by God.
glad - ly live our

2. Be - lives.
3. Be -

7a   The Great 'I Am'

From Exodus 3, John 1 and Ephesians 1 & 3

Hear, God's people, the Lord our God, the Lord is One.
He is the God of Abraham and Sarah,
the God of Isaac, the God of Jacob.
He is the God who says, 'I Am who I Am',
his name for ever and his title for all generations.
He is the God and Father of our Lord Jesus Christ,
the one from whom every family on earth is named.
He is the eternal word, through whom all things were made.
He lived among us, full of grace and truth,
bringing life and light to all creation.
He is the Spirit who strengthens us in our inner being:
he reveals the love of Christ and fills us with the fullness of God.
Hear God's people, the Lord our God is Three in One.
We believe in one God, Father, Son and Holy Spirit.
Amen.

Bigger than the air I breathe
(You)

Tim Hughes, Rob Hill
& Jon Mannson

tell of who___ you are.___ Who can know the mind___ of God?___

Who can un-der-stand___ your ways?___ And these

words are not___ e-nough___ to tell of your___ great name.___

Bridge

You, you, you,___ there's al-ways you,___

___ you, you,___ un-break-a-ble,___ un-shak-a-ble,___ un-beat-a-ble.___

(continued over...)

8a   The Lord is God

The Lord is God, the Lord is One.
Give praise and honour to the Lord.
Praise to God, the one Creator;
he tells us to call him Father!
Praise to God, the only Saviour;
his self-giving love has won us!
And praise the ever-present Spirit
whose life and power and gifts surround us.
To Father, Son and Spirit, praise!
The Lord is God, the Lord is One!

9

Break our hearts
(Raise your voices)

With passion

Andy Flannagan

Verse

1. Break our hearts⏤ and break our si⏤lence,
2. Cease your sing⏤ing, end your danc⏤ing,

may this flesh⏤ spring from the word.⏤
of⏤fer no⏤ more sa⏤ cri-fice.⏤

Shake the dust,⏤ a⏤wa⏤ken lives⏤ that
Strain to hear⏤ the sounds of jus⏤ tice

speak for those⏤ who are ne⏤ver heard.⏤
ris⏤ ing up⏤ to⏤ fight for life.⏤

(continued over...)

10 Bring to God your new best songs

Tune: Gwalchmai

Flowing ♩ = 100

Words: Martin E Leckebusch
Music: J Jones arr. David Peacock

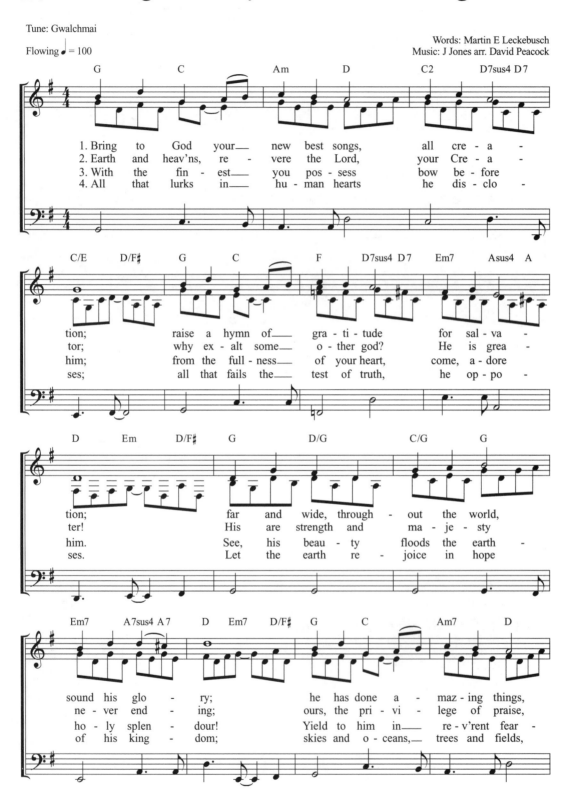

1. Bring to God your new best songs, all cre-a-tion; raise a hymn of gratitude for salvation; far and wide, throughout the world, he has done amazing things,
2. Earth and heav'ns, revere the Lord, your Creator; why exalt some other god? He is greater! His are strength and majesty ours, the privilege of praise,
3. With the finest you possess bow before him; from the fullness of your heart, come, adore him. See, his beauty floods the earth holy splendour! Yield to him in re-v'rent fear-
4. All that lurks in human hearts he discloses; all that fails the test of truth, he opposes. Let the earth rejoice in hope of his kingdom; skies and oceans, trees and fields,

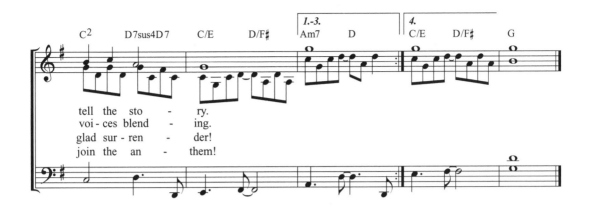

tell the sto - ry.
voi - ces blend - ing.
glad sur - ren - der!
join the an - them!

10a I choose

I choose to follow my experience of meeting Jesus Christ as God of power and might,

God of love and humility, and God of holiness and mercy.

Childish? Simplistic? Possibly.

But can faith be totally rational and sensible?

Faith is making allowance for the inexplicable and the mysterious.

And faith means accepting that God is impossible to explain.

And I really do believe God is much too big to be explained and understood.

It's so hard to fit him into a box – he squeeges out all over.

Childlike I come to God.

In simple trust I stand before his throne

and he receives me with delight on his face and a welcoming embrace!

Not because I deserve anything but because he loves me and chooses to accept me.

That also is beyond reasoning.

Christ's is the world
(A touching place)

Gently but firmly

Words: John L. Bell & Graham Maule
Music: Scottish trad. arr. John L. Bell

Verse

1. Christ's is the world in which we move, Christ's are the
2. Feel for the peo-ple we most a-void: strange, or be-
3. Feel for the par-ents who've lost their child. Feel for the
4. Feel for the lives by life con-fused, rid-dled with

folk we're sum-moned to love, Christ's is the voice that
reaved, or ne-ver em-ployed. Feel for the wo-men and
wo-men whom men have de-filed. Feel for the ba-by for
doubt, in lov-ing a-bused. Feel for the lone-ly heart,

calls us to care, and Christ is the one who meets us here.
feel for the men who fear that their liv-ing is all in vain.
whom there's no breast, and feel for the wea-ry who find no rest.
con-scious of sin, which longs to be pure but fears to be-gin.

Chorus (Harmony)

To the lost Christ shows his face. To the un-loved he

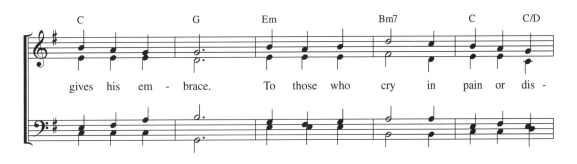

gives his em - brace. To those who cry in pain or dis-

grace,—— Christ makes, with his friends, a touch - ing place.

11a Praise be to the Lamb

Praise be to the blood of the Lamb
in his forgiving power.
Praise be to the blood of the Lamb
in his cleansing power.
Praise be to the blood of the Lamb
in his releasing power.
Praise be to the blood of the Lamb in his victorious power.
By the wounds and the blood of the Lamb,
may God guard and keep us.
Amen.

12 Could I bring your words of comfort
(What Jesus would have done)

David Clifton
& Phil Baggaley

Steady and strong

1. Could I bring your words of com-fort, of-fer peace where there is war, could I bless the ones who curse me, can I for-give the ones who hurt me most?
2. Would I weep if you were weep-ing, walk with those the world dis-owns, can I break the bread of hea-ven, with ev-'ry lost, lost and hun-gry soul?
3. Would I stand a-gainst in-jus-tice, speak for those who can-not speak, be the hands that help the help-less, and be your arms, the arms that hold the weak?
4. Could I lose the life you gave me, lay it down with all I own, will I walk with ev-'ry pil-grim who walked this road, the nar-row way of love?

Lord, I will, so hear my prayer.

Even as the world began
(All over the world)

Capo 4(G)

Matt Redman
& Martin Smith

With energy

1. E - ven as the world be - gan, the stars they sang and all the an - gels
2. Young and old, near and far, there's a place for ev - 'ry heart to

shout - ed for joy, shout - ed for joy. And
join in your song, join in your song.

look - ing back through his - to - ry, your peo - ple they have al - ways had a
Ev - 'ry na - tion, tribe and tongue come to - ge - ther, join as one, give

song they must sing, a song they must sing.
glo - ry to God, give glo - ry to God.

We are the peo - ple of God;
We are the peo - ple of God;

This song is recorded on the Spring Harvest New Songs 'Our God reigns' album

Everlasting God
(Yesterday, today, forever)

Capo 3 (D)

Vicky Beeching

Rock style

(continued over...)

This song is recorded on the Spring Harvest Live Worship 2005 album

40

41

15 Father take me deeper

Steadily

Leigh Barnard

1. Fa-ther take me deep-er still, that I may know you more,
2. Fa-ther take me deep-er still, that I may serve you more,
3. Fa-ther take me deep-er still, that I may love you more,

through your word and teach-ing may I al-ways hold your
keep me stead-fast in your will and guide me through the
though my faith be wea-kened, may I learn to trust you

truth. For all your ways a - bound in love, your
storm. For you a - lone can guard my steps, your
more. How awe-some are your ways, O Lord, how

thoughts are not my own. Fa - ther take me deep - er with you, that
pre - sence shel - ters me. Fa - ther take me deep - er with you, that
faith - ful is our God. Fa - ther take me deep - er with you, that

This song is recorded on the Spring Harvest New Songs 'Sing' album

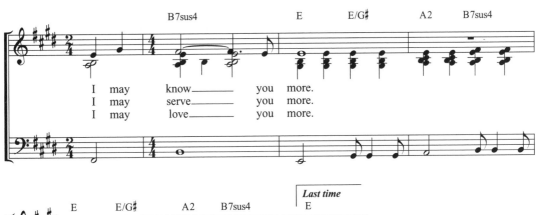

I may know ___ you more.
I may serve ___ you more.
I may love ___ you more.

15a That very night

Based on Matthew 26:33

I loved you, you know I loved you
I stood by you
I was committed, fully committed. All in!

I saw you in your glory Son of God

I gave out loaves and fishes,
I walked on water
I saw the lame walk, and the blind see
I saw you in Gethsemene

That night, I was strong, proclaimed my allegiance
pledged my life!

So close, so committed, so vulnerable

I said I will never never never do that Lord!
But that very same night
I did.

From the highest of heights
(Indescribable)

Capo 3(D)
With strength

Laura Story
Add. lyrics Jesse Reeves

(1st & 2nd time) All po-wer-ful, un-tam-a-ble;
(Last time) In-com-pa-ra-ble, un-change-a-ble,

God._____

awe-struck, we fall to our knees as we hum-bly pro-claim:__ you are a-ma-zing,__
you see the depths of my heart and you love me the__ same,__

God._____   You are a-ma-zing,__ God.____

God._____

D.S. al Coda ⊕ *Coda*

Last time to Coda ⊕

17 Forgive us, Lord
(Hear our song)

Andy Flannagan

Last time to Coda

- ly king - doms,   no in - jus - tice in_____ your name._____

1.2.   D.S.   3.   Bridge

_____   We will feed you,_____ clothe_____ you,   and wel - come__ you in,_____ when will we__ see you__ in our bro-ther's eyes?   When you are thir - sty,__ im - pri - soned__ or ill,_____ we will care.__ When will we   hear you__ in our__

(continued over...)

sis-ter's cries?

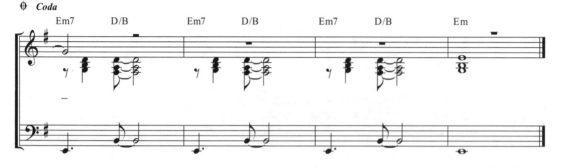

17a A prayer for our nation

O God our heavenly Father, who promises to hear the prayers of your
servants and to help us in our need, we thank you for our country
and for all those who have given of themselves to help us.
We bring before you those who have the responsibility of keeping the
peace and the rule of law in our society, for judges, magistrates and
police. Help them to be diligent in duty, impartial in judgement and
to carry forward the causes of justice and truth.
Open our eyes to the wrong doings around us.
Deepen our concern for the poor and homeless.
We pray for a better nation in which men and women strive not only
to gain their rights but even more to fulfil their responsibilities.
Give us a deep desire to live as your servants, called to be faithful,
to love you and each other and to live in peace. **Amen.**

Giver of life

Tim Hughes

1. Gi - ver of life, you ne - ver change, all that is per - fect comes from you, your won - ders ne - ver cease.

2. Free - ly you give, new e - v'ry - day; your mer - cies will ne - ver fail, so great is your faith - ful - ness.

Not e - ven life, not e - ven death, nor a - ny pow'r
Your love is kind, your love is pure, your love will al -

(continued over...)

This song is recorded on the Spring Harvest New Songs 'Sing' album and the Spring Harvest Distinctive Sounds - Glory album

18a A daily prayer at the beginning of a busy day

Let every meeting we attend be chaired by you, Lord,
let every breath we take be inhaled by the energy of your Spirit,
alone, Lord.
Let every pace that we race be slowed right down by your guiding
hand, Lord.
Assist us to set aside time this day to relax with you, Lord
to respect your presence in our lives, Lord.
May we know your patience,
know your guidance,
know your ways of trust and persuasion.
May we dispel arrogance, pride and inane legislation.
May we fulfil only your purposes which will lead to your glory
and let our personal offerings become together
a worthy sacrifice of praise and thanksgiving.
In the name of Christ
Amen.

19 Go peaceful in gentleness
(Go peaceful)

Paul Field

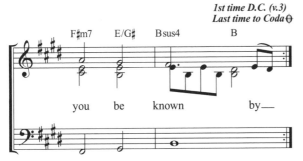

19a In the name of Jesus

In the name of the Father
the name of the Son
and the Holy Ghost
hallowed be that sound
hallowed be the ground
we walk upon in your domain
this little heaven here on earth
this short-stay destination
between birth and death and birth again
between the new-born
the dying the dead and the re-born
hallowed be the name of Jesus
Heavenly body sent to save us
Son of the Father and the Holy Ghost.

20 God above all the world in motion
(Salvation is here)

Joel Houston

1. God a - bove all the world in - mo - tion,_____ God a - bove all my
2. Hear the__ sound of the ge - ne - ra - tions,_____ mak - ing__ loud their__

hopes and__ fears.__ And I don't__ care what the
free - dom__ song.__ All in__ all that the

world throws__ at__ me now,_____ I'm gon-na be al - right.__
world would__ know__ your name._____

be al - right.__ 'Cause I know my__ God___ saved the day.__ And I know__

(continued over...)

21 God Almighty, we look to you
(Call for mercy)

Judy Bailey

Thoughtfully

1. God Al-migh - ty, we look to you,— our hearts are hea-
(2.) mis-sing, for those who wait,— for an - ger that

- vy, so yours must— bleed. We pray for the
threa - tens to turn in - to hate. We pray for your

vic - tims of tra - ge - dy,— that by your grace, O Lord, some-
pre - sence in their— pain, and ask that you re - veal your-

how they'll find re - lief. For all who suf-fer we are call-ing on you, Lord. O—
self in Je - sus' name.

Chorus

(continued over...)

Additional verse:
For nations evading the reality still,
for those steeped in denial,
for the silence that kills;
we pray for the governments that are overwhelmed,
secure their people's future,
shine your light on them.

22 God gave us his Son
(I am not ashamed)

Capo 3(D)

Steadily

Kate & Miles Simmonds

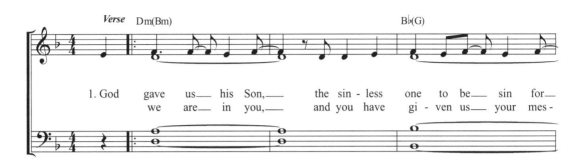

1. God gave us his Son, the sin-less one to be sin for
we are in you, and you have gi-ven us your mes-

us, that we might be the righ-teous-ness of God.
sage to tell the world: be re-con-ciled to God.

Your king-dom has come, we're be-ing changed in-to your like-
Your fa-vour is here in this day of sal-va-tion.

ness; chil-dren of light, it's our time to a-rise.
Now is the time, let your glo-ry a-rise!

(continued over...)

God in my living
(Everything)

Tim Hughes

Capo 4(G)
Gently building

Verse

B(G)   E(C)

1. God in my liv - ing, there in my breath - ing, God in my wak-
   ping, there in my dream - ing, God in my watch-

G#m(Em)   F#(D)

- ing, God in my sleep - ing. God in my rest-
- ing, God in my wait - ing. God in my laugh-

B(G)   E(C)

- ing, there in my work - ing, God in my think-
- ing, there in my weep - ing, God in my hurt-

G#m(Em)   F#(D)

- ing, God in my speak - ing. Be my — ev-'ry-
- ing, God in my heal - ing. Be my — ev-'ry-

E(C)   F#(D)   G#m(Em)   F#(D)   E(C)   F#(D)

thing, be my — ev-'ry - thing; be my — ev-'ry - thing, —— be my — ev-'ry-
thing, be my — ev-'ry - thing, be my — ev-'ry - thing, —— be my — ev-'ry-

This song is recorded on the Spring Harvest New Songs 'Our God reigns' album

Additional choruses:
You are everything . . .
Jesus, everything . . .

God is our refuge and strength
(Psalm 46)

24

Ian White

God____ is our re-fuge and strength, an e-ver pre-sent help in trou-bled times.__ There - fore we will not fear, though the earth__ gives__ way, and the moun-tains fall in - to the heart of the sea, though the wa-ters may roar and the

(continued over...)

25

God, you are my God
(Glory)

Johnny Parks

1. God, you are my God, there's no-one else like you;
2. Death is o-ver-come, for-gi-ven is my sin.

you glad-ly gave your blood, to bring me back to you.
Hea-ven is my home, you've wel-comed me in.

I will sing your praise, I will lift your name,
I can't wait to hear the saints join in one song;

(continued over...)

70

71

26 God of justice
(Cry justice)

Tim Hughes

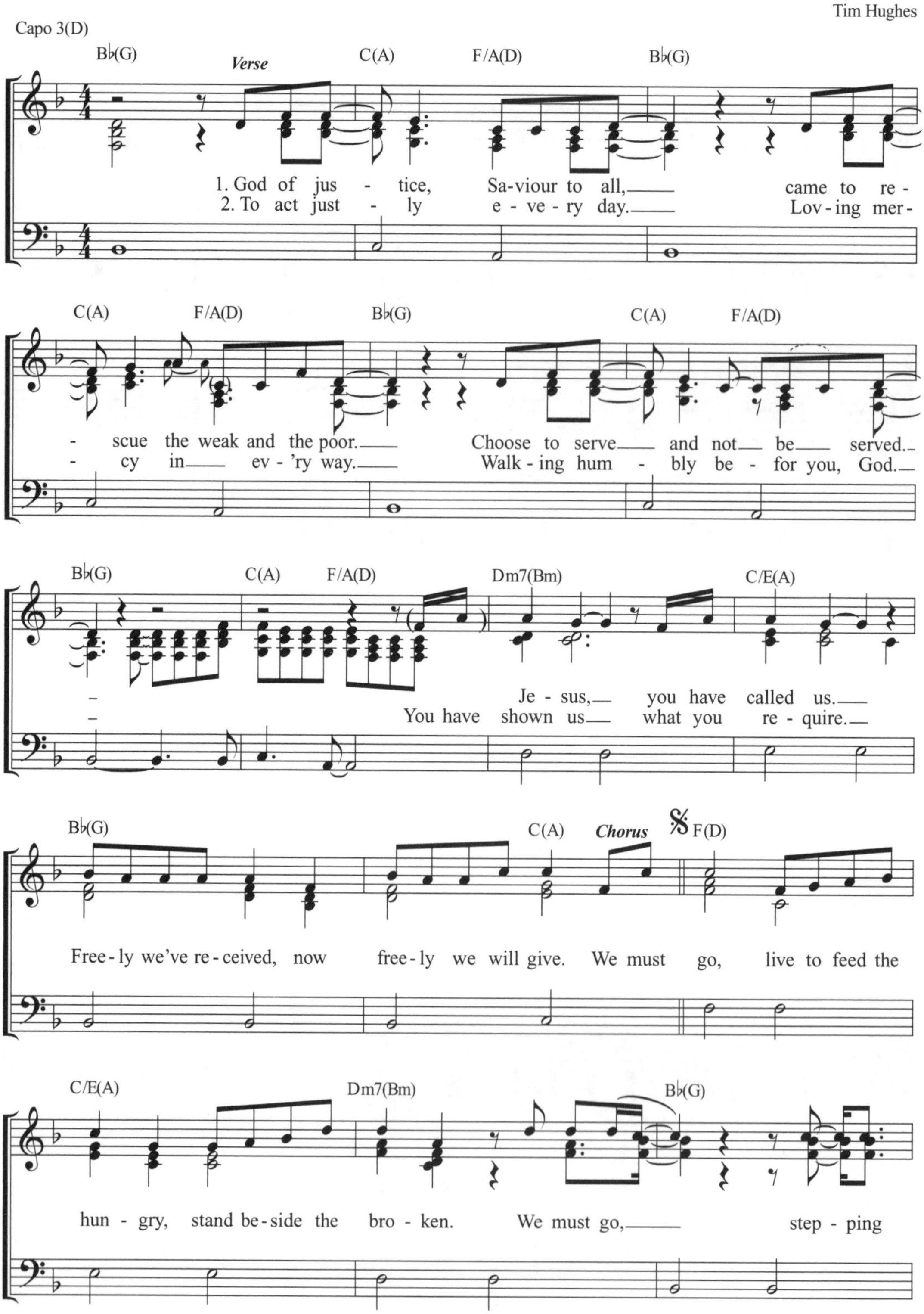

Capo 3(D)
B♭(G) Verse C(A) F/A(D) B♭(G)
1. God of jus - tice, Sa-viour to all, came to re -
2. To act just - ly e - ve - ry day. Lov - ing mer-
C(A) F/A(D) B♭(G) C(A) F/A(D)
- scue the weak and the poor. Choose to serve and not be served.
- cy in ev - 'ry way. Walk - ing hum - bly be - for you, God.
B♭(G) C(A) F/A(D) Dm7(Bm) C/E(A)
Je - sus, you have called us.
You have shown us what you re - quire.
B♭(G) C(A) Chorus F(D)
Free - ly we've re - ceived, now free - ly we will give. We must go, live to feed the
C/E(A) Dm7(Bm) B♭(G)
hun - gry, stand be - side the bro - ken. We must go, step - ping

73

27

God of the mountains
(Creation praise)

Moderately

Sue Rinaldi,
Caroline Bonnett & Steve Bassett

28

God so loved this whole world

Godfrey Birtill

Resolutely

Verse

1. God so loved this whole world that he— gave his on-ly
walk through dark days, where the— earth and hea-vens
cross we are saved, in the— blood we put our

Son, and if we will cleave to him we'll not per -
shake, through the val-ley of de-spair he is with—
faith, for there is no o-ther way in-to hea -

ish; but we'll have e-ter-nal life and we'll— ne-ver be con -
us. Ne-ver giv-ing up on us, faith-ful— and for-e-ver
ven. Je-sus con-quered death and hell, pro-mised— to re-turn a -

demned, for God's pro-mi-ses are yes and a-men!
friend, for God's pro-mi-ses are yes and a-men!
gain, and God's pro-mi-ses are yes and a-men!

Yeah, yeah,

28a Everyday God

God of every time and place
you hold each moment and shape each day;
open our eyes to see you at work,
walk beside us wherever our journeys lead
and strengthen us as your disciples in every area of our lives,
in the power of the Spirit
and in the name of Jesus. **Amen.**

29

Here are my hands

Capo 3 (D)
Steady lilt feel

Danny Cope

30

He's the King of kings
(Our God reigns)

Leigh Barnard

31

Holy One
(God he reigns)

Steady 4

Marty Sampson

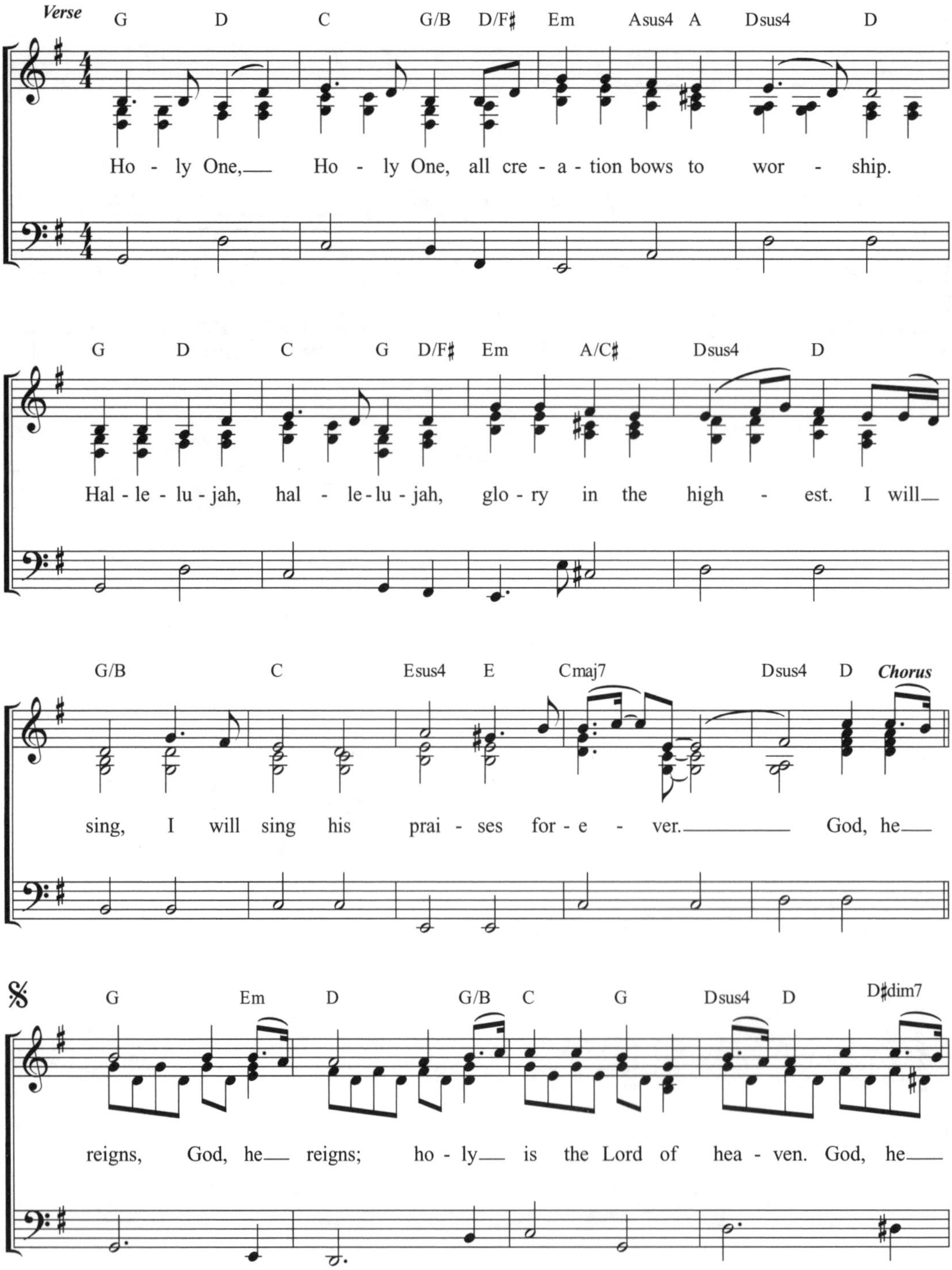
Verse
G D C G/B D/F♯ Em Asus4 A Dsus4 D
Ho - ly One, Ho - ly One, all cre - a - tion bows to wor - ship.
G D C G D/F♯ Em A/C♯ Dsus4 D
Hal - le - lu - jah, hal - le - lu - jah, glo - ry in the high - est. I will
G/B C Esus4 E Cmaj7 Dsus4 D Chorus
sing, I will sing his prai - ses for - e - ver. God, he
G Em D G/B C G Dsus4 D D♯dim7
reigns, God, he reigns; ho - ly is the Lord of hea - ven. God, he

This song is recorded on the Spring Harvest New Songs 'Our God reigns' album.

31a The supremacy of Christ

From Colossians 1: 15–20

He is the image of the invisible God, the firstborn over all creation.
For by him all things were created: things in heaven and on
earth, visible and invisible, whether thrones or powers or rulers or
authorities; all things were created by him and for him. He is before
all things, and in him all things hold together. And he is the head
of the body, the church; he is the beginning and the firstborn from
among the dead, so that in everything he might have the supremacy.
For God was pleased to have all his fulness dwell in him, and through
him to reconcile to himself all things, whether things on earth or
things in heaven, by making peace through his blood, shed on the
cross.

32

Holy Spirit, Breath of heaven

Geraldine Latty

Worshipfully

Holy Spi - rit, Breath of hea - ven, Ho - ly

Spi - rit, breathe on us. Breathe us to a

qui - et still - ness

where we— trust your love for us.
where we— find your place for us.
where we— know that you are God.

This song is recorded on the Spring Harvest New Songs 'Sing' album

The use of short songs in worship

Short musical units, repeated a number of times, can enrich worship in various ways. Sometimes these units are called 'chants', particularly if sung continuously during a time of reflection or contemplative prayer. Sometimes they can be sung responses (e.g. with spoken intercessions). A short song like 'Our God is an awesome God' gain in impact through imaginative repetition. Look through this songbook for other examples of short songs.

Some ideas for using this kind of material:
- Repeating a phrase, with words appropriate to the season or the theme of a service, while people gather for worship.
- As a way of helping people to focus on God while different visual images are displayed.
- To ease the transition between exuberant sung praise and quieter adoration, silent prayer, a reading or a sermon.
- Continuous singing of a simple expression of trust amidst pain, when a community is bewildered or grieving.
- To accompany some kind of symbolic action (receiving bread and wine, lighting a candle at a prayer station, untying a piece of knotted string as an expression of commitment to working for justice).
- Interspersing spoken petitions with a musical response to engage the emotions as well as the mind and foster the participation of all in prayer.
- Enabling reflection on a particular aspect of a Bible passage by singing an appropriate phrase at intervals during the reading or at the end.
- To accompany movement, perhaps to another part of the building or as the congregation leaves.

Some practicalities:
- Short songs taught by rote can be useful in all-age worship and other contexts where literacy levels vary or different languages are spoken.
- If people are going to hear and sing the same phrase many times, it needs to have depth as well as simplicity – consider the quality of words and musical sounds, to avoid banality and boredom.
- Using vocal harmony and instrumental descants, whether written out or improvised, can transform a simple song.
- Where musical repetition is open-ended, the worship leader may need to think how it's going to stop!

Anne Harrison
Co-ordinator for *Sunday by Sunday* (published quarterly by the Royal School of Church Music)

33 How can we talk about forgiveness
(Still forgive)

Paul Field & Dan Wheeler

This song was written following the London terrorist bombs 7th July 2005.

con-ciled, how can____ we walk____ the ex - tra mile____
_ no grace, we're left hang - ing by____ a thread of faith
ken heart. Where____ can hope____ and heal - ing start____

to find__ the love?____
to find__ the love.__
to find__ the love?__

_ For it all____ comes down____ to this:____

can we find the love,____ to take the hurt,____ still for-give.____

Yes it all____ comes down____ to this:____

(continued over...)

to find the love,___ take the hurt,___ still for-give.___

When we see the brid - ges turn___ to dust,___ can we build them up

a - gain, can we build___ them up?___ Can we

swal-low wound - ed pride,___ put our pre - ju - dice___ a - side,___ reach a-

33a I fall Lord

Based on Psalm 141

I fall Lord, I keep falling
But you keep forgiving

I try Lord, I keep trying
And you keep cheering

I hurt Lord, I keep hurting
But you keep loving

I pray Lord, I'll keep praying
For you keep listening

34 I have seen a mystery
(It is the church)

Lex Loizides

With a strong beat

Verse

I have seen a mys-te-ry, the hopes of pray'r and
Re - scued, ran - somed, lif - ted up, crowned with mer - cy,

pro - phe - cy, and ris-ing from all peo-ples see, she comes.___
clothed in hope, the ob-ject of all hea-ven's love, she comes.___

1. 2.

Chorus

It is the church,___ the
the

hope of all___ the world,___ and here___ I fix___ my heart___
pas - sion of___ God's Son,___ the goal___ of hi - st'ry, come.___

___ and hand,___ I can - not turn___ a - way!
___ You'll see___ we've near - ly reached___ the___ day.

35 Image of invisible God

Stuart Townend
& J.K. Jamieson

Steadily, with majesty

1. I - mage of in - vi - si - ble God,____ cre - a - tor and su - stai - ner of all;____ the King who came to ran - som my soul,____ thank you for your per - fect love.____
2. Ho - ly One whom an - gels at - tend,____ righ - teous King who calls me his friend;____ the Prince who of - fers peace with - out end,____ thank you for your per - fect love.____
3. There - fore I will not be a - fraid,____ though moun - tains fall and ri - vers may rage;____ I'm safe with - in the ci - ty you've made,____ thank you for your per - fect love.____

1st time D.C.

Chorus

And it's

93

I lay my life down
(One way)

36

Capo 2 (A)

Joel Houston
& Jonathon Douglass

(continued over...)

F#(E) E(D) *1.-3.* *4.* *D.S. al Coda*

-ing all— for you.———————— — Here we go.

Coda

G#m7(F#m7) A2(G2) B(A)

You're the on-ly one that   I could live for.———

36a As we gather

God the Father, God the Creator
Be with us as we gather
God the Son, Christ the Saviour
Be with us as we give thanks
God the Spirit, Holy and powerful
Be with us as we worship

37 In the Lord I'll be ever thankful

Words: Taizé Community
Music: Jacques Berthier (1923-1994)

Capo 3(D)

♩ = 69

In Him I have believed

Capo 3 (D)

Kate Simmonds

dark - ness in - to your good - ness, we are your chil - dren,
on in the pow'r of your Spi - rit, tak - ing your go - spel
nat - ion your king - dom ad - van - ces; who can ex - tin - guish
bra - tion! The glo - ri - ous u - nion: The Li - on of Ju - dah

cho - sen in Christ. Now in your fa - mily,
to all the world, de - clar - ing your wis - dom,
this spread - ing flame? Through tri - bu - la - tions
and the pure, spot - less bride! All of cre - a - tion

heirs of the pro - mise, to your pur - pose on the
our great com - mis - sion, that Je - sus Christ has
we'll stand on your pro - mise: 'I will build my church and
waits for this mo - ment, all your pro - mi - ses ful -

earth I give my life.
come to save the lost.
hell will not pre - vail!'
filled in Je - sus Christ!

39

In this fallen world
(Let your kingdom come)

Capo 3(G)

Jon Bilbrough

(continued over...)

40

In your world
your kingdom come, O Lord

Simon Bray

1. In your world — your king-dom come, O Lord;
2. In your church — your king-dom come, O Lord;
3. In my heart — your king-dom come, O Lord;

may your — will be done on earth.
may your — will be done in us.
may your — will be done in me.

40a Prayer for renewal

Most merciful Lord we ask for our nation a renewal of true faith, a recovery of Christian virtue and a return to the paths of righteousness. Stir up in each of us sincere love and responsibility to one another and bring our nation to know and love you, the God of true mercy, love and forgiveness, through Jesus Christ our Lord. **Amen.**

Into your hands I commit again
(With all I am)

Reuben Morgan

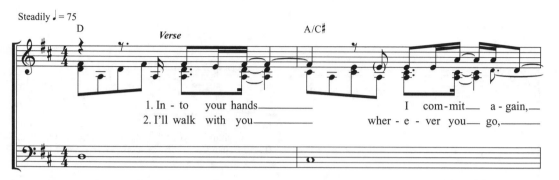

1. In-to your hands_____ I com-mit a-gain,_____
2. I'll walk with you_____ wher-e-ver you go,_____

_____ all I am_____ for you, Lord._____ You hold my world_____
_____ through tears and joy,_____ I'll trust in you. And I will live_____

_____ in the palm of your hand,_____ and I am yours_____ for-e-ver._____
_____ in all of your ways,_____ and your pro-mi-ses_____ for-e-ver._____

Je-sus, I be-lieve_____ in you._____

41a I love your company

I love your company, I delight in your presence,
I created you to spend time with me,
to enjoy my love and marvel at my glory.
When you stop to pray, leave words aside for a while – you'll find you
don't always need them.   *(pause)*

Stay awhile enjoy my presence marvel at my glory.
See the radiance of my face and robes, my angels cry 'Glory!'
My light purifies your soul, and we smile at each other in wonder.

Yes, bow your head!
I am mighty, I am awesome,
I am the Creator and the sustainer of the universe!
If I cease to be, so do you – you have your every minute at my
command.

I am majestic, powerful, all-glorious,
and I sent my Son to love you, and to woo you,
so you could love me too.

42

I've had questions
(When the tears fall)

Tim Hughes

Verse

1. I've had ques-tions with-out an-swers, I've known sor-row, I have known pain.— But there's one thing, that I'll cling to; you are faith-ful, Je-sus, you're true.—

2. In the lone hour of my sor-row, through the dark-est night of my soul,— you sur-round me and sus-tain me; my de-fen-der, for-e-ver more.—

Chorus

When hope is lost, I'll call you Sa-viour.— When pain sur-rounds, I'll call you heal-er.—

(continued over...)

This song is recorded on the Spring Harvest New Songs 'Sing' album and the Spring Harvest Live Worship 2004 album

I'll call you Sa - viour.___ When pain sur-rounds, I'll call you heal - er.___

When si-lence falls, you'll be the song with-in my___ heart.___

42a God to enfold me

*Psalm 5:11–12, Isaiah 43:10–11
and Revelation 1:8*

God to enfold me, God to surround me,
God in my speaking, God in my thinking,
God in my sleeping, God in my waking,
God in my watching, God in my hoping,
God in my life, God in my lips,
God in my soul, God in my heart,
God in my sufficing, God in my slumber,
God in mine ever-living soul, God in mine eternity.

I will glory in my Redeemer

43

Steve & Vikki Cook

1. I will glo-ry— in—my Re-
deem-er,— whose price-less blood has ran-somed me. Mine was the sin that drove the
bit-ter nails, and hung him on that—judge-ment tree. I will glo-ry— in my Re-
deem-er,— who crushed the pow'r of sin and death, my on-ly

glo-ry— in—my Re-
deem-er,— my life he bought, my love he owns. I have no long-ings for a-
no-ther, I'm sa-tis-fied in—him a-lone. I will glo-ry— in my Re-
deem-er,— his faith-ful-ness my stand-ing place. Though foes are

glo-ry— in—my Re-
deem-er,— who car-ries me on ea-gle's wings. He crowns my life with lov-ing
kind-ness, his tri-umph song I'll— e-ver sing. I will glo-ry— in my Re-
deem-er,— who waits for me at gates of gold, and when he

I will set my face
(Wonderful God)

Godfrey Birtill

Capo 3(D)

With life

Chorus I will set my face to seek the Lord, I will set my face to seek the Lord, give my full at-ten-tion to my God, I will lis-ten for his voice, I will lis-ten for his voice.

Verse

1. My won-der-ful counsel-lor, my tea-cher, re-min-der, re-vea-ler, my heal-er, my streng-then-er, re-pair-er, re-fi-ner, my Je-sus, my
run-ner and fin-ish-er, my con-quer-or, de-li-ve-rer, re-stor-er, my an-chor, my fi-re, u-ni-ter, Re-deem-er, my Je-sus, my

2. Cre-a-tor, de-fen-der, my ma-ker, in-struc-tor, com-man-der, my war-rior, my shel-ter, my help-er, my lead-er, my Je-sus, my
shep-herd, my ga-ther-er, re-fresh-er, re-ward-er, pro-tec-tor, in-spir-er, pro-vi-der, my por-tion, for-e-ver, My Je-sus, my

45 Jesus Christ, Perfect Love
(Perfect Love)

Geraldine Latty & busbee

Thoughtfully

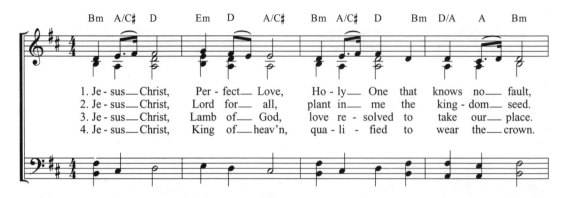

1. Je - sus— Christ, Per - fect— Love, Ho - ly— One that knows no— fault,
2. Je - sus— Christ, Lord for— all, plant in— me the king - dom— seed.
3. Je - sus— Christ, Lamb of— God, love re - solved to take our— place.
4. Je - sus— Christ, King of— heav'n, qua - li - fied to wear the— crown.

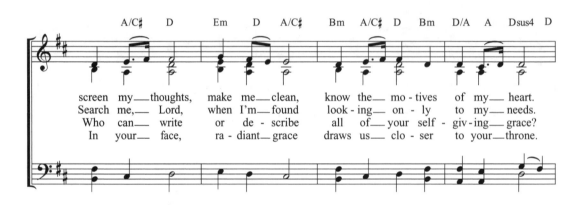

screen my— thoughts, make me— clean, know the— mo - tives of my— heart.
Search me,— Lord, when I'm— found look - ing— on - ly to my— needs.
Who can— write or de - scribe all of— your self - giv - ing— grace?
In your— face, ra - diant— grace draws us— clo - ser to your— throne.

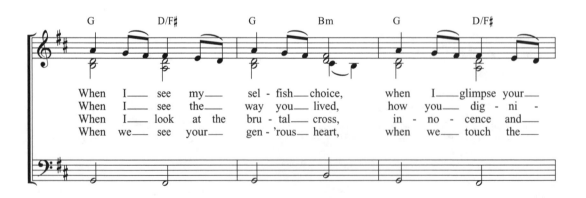

When I— see my— sel - fish— choice, when I— glimpse your—
When I— see the— way you— lived, how you— dig - ni -
When I— look at the— bru - tal— cross, in - no - cence and—
When we— see your— gen - 'rous— heart, when we— touch the—

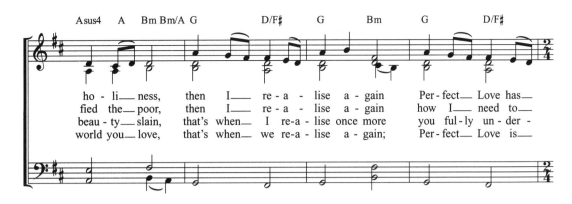

ho - li—ness, then I— re - a - lise a - gain Per- fect— Love has—
fied the— poor, then I— re - a - lise a - gain how I— need to—
beau - ty— slain, that's when I re-a - lise once more you ful-ly un - der -
world you— love, that's when— we re-a - lise a - gain; Per- fect— Love is—

come to— cleanse.
know you— more.
stand our— pain.
Per - fect— Hope.

45a God the One for all

God the One for all,
I don't understand how you made everything
I don't understand how you led your people
I don't understand how you did miracles
I don't understand how you spoke words of wisdom
I don't understand how you keep going
I don't understand how you went through a painful death.
God, the One for all,
I don't understand your love, but I am happy to receive it. **Amen.**

46

Jesus, hope of the nations
(Hope of the nations)

Strong rhythm

Brian Doerksen

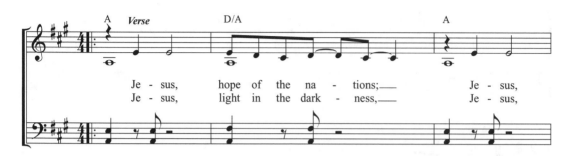

Je-sus, hope of the na - tions;___ Je-sus,
Je-sus, light in the dark - ness,___ Je-sus,

com-fort for all___ who mourn,___ you are___ the source___ of hea-
truth in each cir - cum-stance,___ you are___ the source___ of hea-

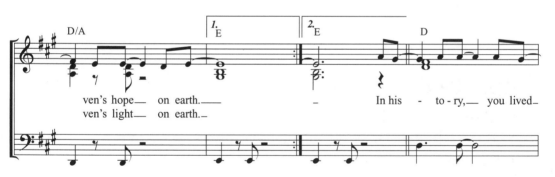

ven's hope___ on earth.___ In his - to-ry,___ you lived___
ven's light___ on earth.___

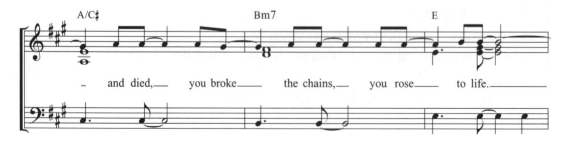

_ and died,___ you broke___ the chains,___ you rose___ to life.___

47
Jesus, I could sing
(If I have not love)

Matt Redman

1. Je-sus, I could sing in the tongues of men and an-gels, but if I have not love I am just a clang-ing cym-bal, an emp-ty sound. just a clang-ing cym-bal, an emp-ty sound.

(2.) Je-sus, I could pray with a faith that moves a moun-tain, but if I have not love it is just a noise re-sound-ing, an emp-ty sound. 2. And just a noise re-sound-ing, an emp-ty sound.

(3.) o-ver-flow of hearts, as we gaze up-on your beau-ty, a re-flec-tion of your worth, for we've seen a glimpse of you in your glo-ry, Lord. 3. It's the seen a glimpse of you in your glo-ry, Lord.

Repeat verse each time

(Fine)

Chorus This is a love song, this is a love

song,— Je-sus, a love——— song— to— you.——— A song of de-vo-

-tion,——— a re-ve-rent pas - sion,— Sa-viour, a love—

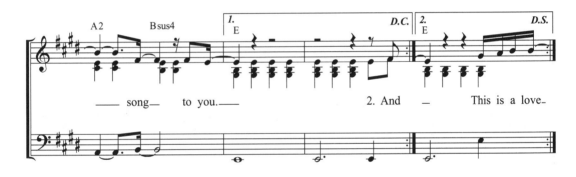

song— to you.——— 2. And — This is a love—

— 3. It's the

48

Jesus, Jesus, Holy One
(Glorify your name)

David Holmes
& Darlene Zschech

Slowly

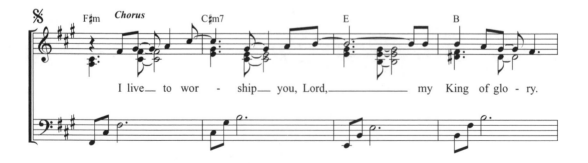

Brought me— to life,— gave— me wings— to fly: you are ho - ly.—

Hea-ven— and earth— de-clare— your praise.— Both

now and e - ver-more,— I glor - i-fy— your— name.—

Last time to Coda ✛

now and e - ver-more,— I glor - i-fy— your— name.—

✛ *Coda*

——— Both now and e - ver-more,— I glor - i-fy— your— name.—

121

49

Jesus, your name

Simple and powerful

Keith and Kristyn Getty
& Ian Hannah

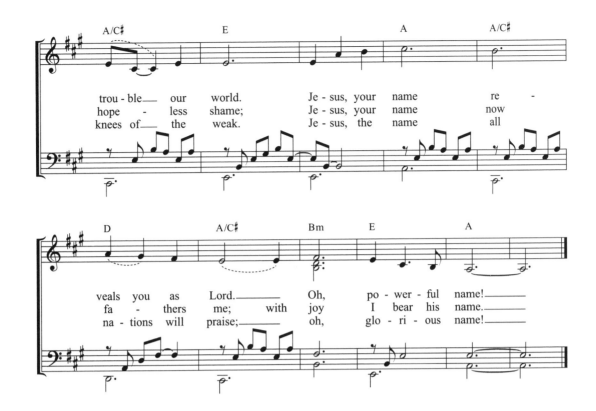

trou-ble— our world. Je-sus, your name re-
hope-less shame; Je-sus, your name now
knees of— the weak. Je-sus, the name all

veals you as Lord.— Oh, po-wer-ful name!—
fa-thers me; with joy I bear his name.—
na-tions will praise;— oh, glo-ri-ous name!—

49a Father in heaven

Based on Matthew 6:9

Father in heaven hallowed be your name

Honoured, revered, respected be your name
I thoughtfully, consciously, gratefully utter your name
The name above all names
The Lord of lords, King of kings, Almighty God, El Shaddai.

Who holds all authority and power
who created the heavens and the earth
who created my inmost being
who desires to be known as...

Father.

50 King of angels, King of saints
(Praise you)

Paul Oakley

com - pares___ with you,___ so I bow___ in awe___ of you.___ And I praise___ King.___

126

51 Left my fear by the side of the road
(All I need is you)

Marty Sampson

(continued over...)

128

-ni-verse,_____ you hold_____ ev'ry-one_ on earth,_____ you hold_

_ the u - ni-verse,_____ you hold,_____ you hold._

You hold_ _ You hold._____ All I need is

D.S. al Fine

51a Jesus, our friend

Dear Lord Jesus, gentle friend
you will never let us down
you will never leave us or betray us
you help us and will continue to do so.
You protect our tongues from rude and unkind words
and you assist us to turn away from bullying tendencies.
When we seek your blessing, you freely offer us forgiveness.
You will help us each day to learn more of you
and in how to care for others and your world
Lord, Jesus, please help us in this moment of worship,
now and always.
Amen.

Let all, all thanksgiving
(The Lord our God is One)

Graham Kendrick

This song is recorded on the Spring Harvest New Songs 'Our God reigns' album

there's no - one else,— the high and Ho - ly One;— so love the Lord—

with all— your— soul and strength: the Lord our God— is

One, the Lord our God— is One. One.

Last time
G *(Fine)*

1.3. 3rd time to Coda
Dsus4

2.
Dsus4 D

Bridge

2. Let O - ther gods than you have ruled— us,
3. Let

op-pressed us, and con - trolled— us. Yet, you came, and with your

(continued over...)

blood   you bought us   back: now all our   chains are bro - ken.   all,   all the

glo - ry   be   gi - ven   to   you, our Lord. To   Fa - ther, Son   and   Spi - rit,   for-

e - ver,   to   God,   the Three_____ in One._____

Songs of justice

Throughout the Old Testament, it is proclaimed that God's reign is based on the dual foundations of justice and righteousness. When we speak or sing of God's passion for justice, and the implications of that in our own lives, we are not just paying lip service to another noble cause that the church is becoming involved in, but prophetically speaking of the nature of the King and his coming Kingdom.

Often songs based around justice themes will have sprung from a particular context. For instance 'Hear our song' (no.17) was written after experiencing the negative legacy of Britain's empire and the West's continuing culpability in Bangladesh. It is often helpful to explain these contexts, perhaps with still images or video material. Try to integrate these songs into your regular 'canon' rather than always making them a special event.

Avoid the temptation that all worship leaders face to simply 'give the people what they want'. Often justice-themed songs do not provide the 'warm fuzzy, holy moment' that can sometimes seem to be the goal of modern worship. Sometimes you have to hold your nerve, believing that the place that includes anger, confusion, grief and sorrow is just as valid a place in worship as happy, content and victorious. Avoid the temptation to use another song to 'get everyone up' again!

The words of Amos chapter 5:21–24 speak powerfully enough on their own, but they might hit even closer to home if they read like this…

'I hate your festivals. I cannot stand your worship events. Even though there are thousands of people, and the PA could cause an earthquake, I will not accept them. Even though the band is fantastic, and you have the best worship leader in the world, I have no regard for them. Do you think I care who sells most CDs? Do you think I care what the 'cool new song' is? Away with this individualised, feel-good soundtrack of iPOD "worship". I'm listening online to another channel. It's called Justice and Righteousness, and it's arriving on a broadband connection that is wider than you could ever imagine. That's what I want to hear. I know when someone's playing MY song.'

God invites us to be part of 'bringing in' his Kingdom of justice and righteousness. In modern worship contexts there are often opportunities to turn our prayers and singing outwards such as crying out for the poor of the world. This may be from a place of compassion, having been broken by images or stories, but this may also be from a place of anger, having been informed of the injustices in our global economic system. Jesus engaged his heart both in weeping for a dead friend and his family, and in throwing over the tables of the money-changers in the temple. We need to listen for God's heartbeat, that it might become our own, so that his compassion and anger pulses through our veins as we sing, that the words of Ezekiel 11 would be proved true – *'I will give them an undivided heart and put a new spirit in them; I will remove from them their heart of stone and give them a heart of flesh.'*

Andy Flannagan www.andyflan.com
See the Thematic Index for more examples of justice songs in this book.

53

Let the power of the gospel flow over me

Marc James

Steadily

1. Let the po - wer of the gos - pel flow o - ver me. Let the
   love___ of the Fa - ther be seen in me. Let the
   po - wer of the Spi - rit move o - ver me. Let the

po - wer of the gos - pel flow o - ver me.___ Let the
love___ of the Fa - ther be seen in me.___ Let the
po - wer of the Spi - rit move o - ver me.___ Let the

po - wer of the go - spel___ flow o - ver me, Je - sus flow o - ver me.
love___ of the Fa - ther___ be seen in me, Fa - ther be seen in me.
po - wer of the Spi - rit___ move o - ver me, Spi - rit move o - ver me.

Chorus

So the blind___ can___ see, the dead___ can rise,___ see the

chil-dren com - ing home— to find— their Fa - ther's eyes.— With strength to the

weak, love— to the least,— the op - pressed and the cap - tive be— set free,–

_ (be set free.) 2. Let the free, free.
3. Let the

1.2.

Last time

54

Lift up your gaze
(King of glory)

Chris Tomlin & Jesse Reeves

1. Lift up your gaze, be lif - ted up,— tell ev - 'ry one how great—the love,
hands, be lift - ed up,— let the re - deemed de - clare—the love.

the love come down from hea - ven's gate to kiss the
And we bow down at hea - ven's gate to kiss the

earth with hope—and grace. Sing: Who is— this King———of glo - ry?—
feet of hope—and grace. *Last chorus: You are— the King———of glo - ry.—*

The Lord,— strong——and migh - ty!——— 2. Lift up your
The Lord,— strong——and migh - ty!———

There is one God; he is ho-ly. There is one Lord o-ver ev-'ry-thing, there is one King, he is Je-sus, King of glo-ry, strong and migh-ty! There is and migh-ty!

54a What a God we worship!

Leader	What a God we worship!
Group A	He has always known us; he is our Maker.
Group B	He has always loved us; he is our Saviour.
Group A	In our darkest hours he is our light;
Group B	In our fiercest fight he is our shield.
Group A	When we need direction, he is our guide;
Group B	When our joy runs dry, he is our song.
Group A	At the point of despair, he is our hope;
Group B	at the moment of danger, he is our refuge.
Group A	He is just and true, loving and merciful;
Group B	He is Rock and Shepherd, King and Father.
All	What a God we serve!

Light of God, come dwell
within your people
(Light of God)

Moderate 2

Keith & Kristyn Getty

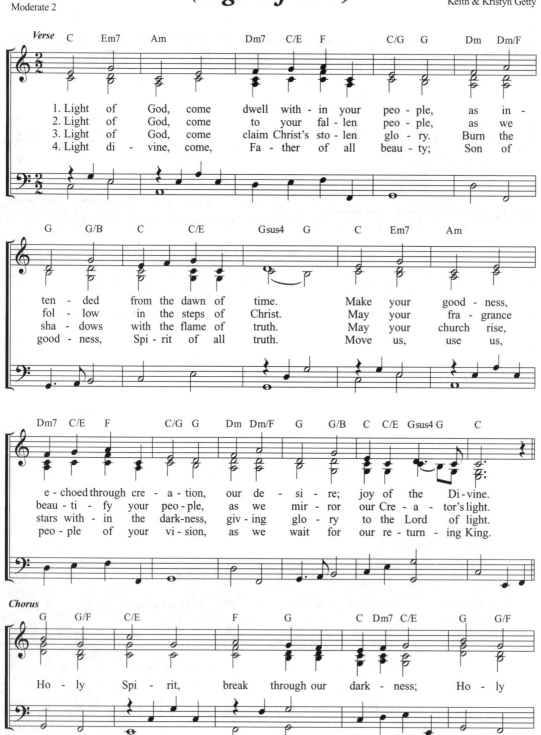

Verse

1. Light of God, come dwell with - in your peo - ple, as in - tend - ed from the dawn of time. Make your good - ness, e - choed through cre - a - tion, our de - si - re; joy of the Di - vine.

2. Light of God, come to your fal - len peo - ple, as we fol - low in the steps of Christ. May your fra - grance beau - ti - fy your peo - ple, as we mir - ror our Cre - a - tor's light.

3. Light of God, come claim Christ's sto - len glo - ry. Burn the sha - dows with the flame of truth. May your church rise, stars with - in the dark - ness, giv - ing glo - ry to the Lord of light.

4. Light di - vine, come, Fa - ther of all beau - ty; Son of good - ness, Spi - rit of all truth. Move us, use us, peo - ple of your vi - sion, as we wait for our re - turn - ing King.

Chorus

Ho - ly Spi - rit, break through our dark - ness; Ho - ly

Spi - rit, breathe through our lives. Light of God, come,

ra - diant and glo - rious; per - fect wis - dom in this world to - day.

56 Long before we were created
(Grace)

Geraldine Latty

1. Long be-fore we were cre - a - ted,
2. We're a part of his own fam - ily,
3. This is our Fa - ther's sto - ry,

at the dawn of space and time, God e - ter - nal, great and migh - ty
sim - ply through the love of Christ, what a per - fect, all em - brac - ing,
this is our Ma - ker's praise, and by the Spi - rit we're the

had us on his mind. He de - vised and set be - fore us,
self - less sa - cri - fice. God has thought of e - v'ry op - tion,
sto - ry of his grace. Us - ing or - di - na - ry peo - ple,

an a - ma - zing, per - fect plan, that would de - mon - strate to all the
he's pro - vi - ded all we need; that the weak, the strong, the rich, the
us - ing bro - ken jars of clay, he'll dis - play the grace that e - ven

141

57

Lord draw near and stay

John L. Bell

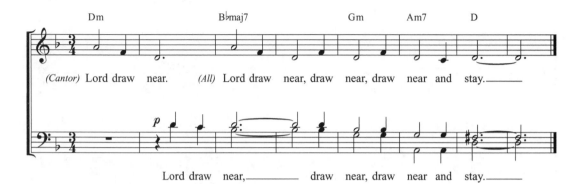

(Cantor) Lord draw near. (All) Lord draw near, draw near, draw near and stay.

Lord draw near, draw near, draw near and stay.

57a Encircled by the Lord

Lord God, some things make us angry
some things make us burn
some things make us fearful and tearful
some things make us yearn.
Some things bring us alarm and how vulnerable we sometimes feel
in the shadow of death.
Yet, good Shepherd of the sheep, you stay with us Lord,
especially when evil still lurks as the day draws to a close
you stay with us Lord,
no stalemate, no trickery, no jeers, no hate;
simply the overriding light of your presence returns.
Your arms encircle us all ways round, Lord
you extend the unceasing rainbow promise of your covenant love,
Lord.
And by the power of the resurrection and your Spirit
you remain the one true God.
Our Saviour – Jesus alone, Christ,
one God, one Church, one people for you alone, Lord.
One Yahweh, the Alpha, the Omega,
the source and the light. **Amen.**

Copyright © 2005 Marie Birkinshaw

58

Lord, here we are
(You are the One)

Tré & Tori Sheppard

Lord,— here we are,— sons and daugh-ters of your hand,—

here, wait-ing for you, with our hearts and with our plans.— So

come, fill us with faith, fill us with peace— once a-gain.—

Come, fill us with hope, fill us with won-der and— with love. you are the

one, you are the one, you are the one, on-ly one.

(continued over...)

This song is recorded on the Spring Harvest New Songs 'Our God reigns' album.

58a I thirst for you

Based on Psalm 42

Lord I thirst for you
I long to know your living water.

Not to wait at the edge... and wonder
Not to gaze though beauty restores my soul
Not to paddle though refreshing ripples calm me.

But to wade and keep wading
Till I am carried on your current and the depths are deeper.

Your river is strong, your river is safe
Your river is life.

Lord of all creation
(God of wonders)

Capo 1(G)

Marc Byrd
& Steve Hindalong

With praise

Lyrics:

1. Lord of all creation, of water, earth and sky, the heavens are your tabernacle; glory to the Lord on high.

2. Early in the morning I will celebrate the light, and as I stumble in the darkness I will call your name by night.

God of wonders beyond our galaxy, you are holy, holy; the universe declares your majesty. You are

This song is recorded on the Spring Harvest New Songs 2004/05 album

60

Love unfailing
(To the ends of the earth)

Joel Houston & Marty Sampson

Moderate pace

Verse

Love un-fail - ing, o - ver-tak - ing my heart.___ You

take me___ in,___ find-ing peace___ a-gain,___ fear is lost in all you___

_ are.___ And I would give___ the world to tell your sto-

- ry, 'cause I know that you've called___ me,___ I know that you've called___

_ me.___ I've lost my-self___ for good with-in your pro - mise, and I won't hide___

61 Love so amazing

Capo 3(G)

Wayne Sanders

life   to re-deem mine,_____   paid as a ran - som   so I could go free:____

Last time to Coda

love so a- maz-ing,   so— di-vine,____   gi-ven for me.____

1.   *D.C.*   *2.*

2. Love so a-

Bridge

When I think what you've done for— me,   I am o-ver-come with praise;

your grace has co-vered my shame,_____   I be-lieve   in the pow'r

(continued over...)

151

62

My Saviour, Redeemer
(For all you've done)

Reuben Morgan

My Sa - viour,_____ Re - dee - mer,_____ lif - ted me from the mi - ry clay._____ Al - migh - ty,_____ for - e - ver,_____ I will ne - ver be the same, 'cause you_____ came near,_____ from the e - ver - last - ing_____ to the world_____ we_____ live,_____ the Fa - ther's on - ly Son._____

And you lived and you died, and you rose a - gain_____ on high,_____

(continued over...)

154

62a In every place and in every age

From Daniel 2: 20–22

Praise the name of the living God,
in every place and in every age.
God is the source of wisdom and power
in every place and in every age.
God determines times and seasons
in every place and in every age.
God brings light to search the darkness
in every place and in every age.
God gives knowledge and understanding
in every place and in every age.
Praise the name of the living God,
in every place and in every age.

63

My soul sings
(All that I want)

Mike Gulielmucci

1. My soul sings to my Saviour, King of kings. Oh I need you, you are ev-'ry - thing to me.

2. I love you so much more than a - ny - thing, and I'll live for you, Je-sus, you are ev - 'ry - thing.

You're all that I want, you're all that I need, you're all that I want, you're all that I live for in this

64

My troubled soul
(Praise the mighty name of Jesus)

Capo 3 (G)

Robert Critchley

Gently

Verse My— trou-bled soul, why so weighed down? You were— not made— to bear— this hea-vy load.— Cast all your bur - dens up-on— the Lord;— Je-sus cares, he cares— for you.— Je-sus cares,— he cares for you.— And all your wor-ry-ing—won't help you make— it through.

(continued over...)

D.S. al Fine

64a In the good and the hard times

Be with me in the good times, help me in the hard times.
When I am feeling good and nothing seems to go wrong
Be with me in the good times, help me in the hard times.
When everything I touch works out right, and everyone likes me
Be with me in the good times, help me in the hard times.
When times are hard and I seem to make mistakes
Be with me in the good times, help me in the hard times.
When I suffer pain and hurt, and I can't see an end
Be with me in the good times, help me in the hard times.
When everything is exciting, and when everything is dull
Be with me in the good times, help me in the hard times.
When I love you with all my heart, and when I forget all about you
Be with me in the good times, help me in the hard times.

65

Nothing can trouble

Music: J. Berthier (1923-1994)

♩ = 72

No-thing can trou - ble, no-thing can fright - en, those who seek God shall

ne - ver go want - ing. No-thing can trou - ble, no-thing can fright - en,

God a - lone fills us.

O church arise

Stuart Townend & Keith Getty

Resolutely

1. O church, a - rise, and put your ar - mour on; hear the
2. Our call to war, to love the cap - tive soul, but to
3. Come see the cross, where love and mer - cy meet, as the
4. So Spi - rit, come, put strength in ev - 'ry stride, give____

call of Christ our cap - tain. For now the weak can say that
rage a - gainst the cap - tor; and with the sword that makes the
Son of God is stric - ken; then see his foes lie crushed be -
grace for ev - 'ry hur - dle, that we may run with faith to

they are strong in the strength that God has giv - en. With shield of
wound - ed whole, we will fight with faith and va - lour. When faced with
neath his feet, for the Con - que - ror has ri - sen! And as the
win the prize of a ser - vant good and faith - ful. As saints of

faith and belt of truth, we'll stand a - gainst the de - vil's
trials on ev - 'ry side, we know the out - come is se -
stone is rolled a - way, and Christ e - mer - ges from the
old still line the way, re - tel - ling tri - umphs of his

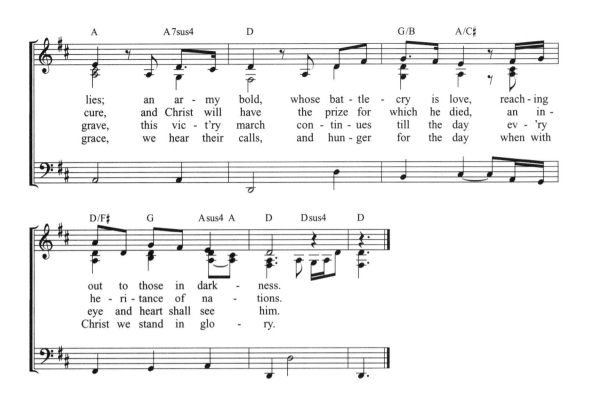

lies;   an ar - my bold, whose bat - tle - cry is love, reach - ing
cure,   and Christ will have the prize for which he died, an in -
grave,   this vic - t'ry march con - tin - ues till the day ev - 'ry
grace,   we hear their calls, and hun - ger for the day when with

out to those in dark - ness.
he - ri - tance of na - tions.
eye and heart shall see him.
Christ we stand in glo - ry.

66a The armour of God

Ephesians 6: 10–17

Finally, be strong in the Lord and in his mighty power. Put on the full armour of God so that you can take your stand against the devil's schemes. For our struggle is not against flesh and blood, but against the rulers, against the powers of this dark world and against the spiritual forces of evil in the heavenly realms.

Therefore put on the full armour of God, so that when the day of evil comes, you may be able to stand your ground, and after you have done everything, to stand. Stand firm then, with the belt of truth buckled round your waist, with the breastplate of righteousness in place, and with your feet fitted with the readiness that comes from the gospel of peace.

In addition to all this, take up the shield of faith, with which you can extinguish all the flaming arrows of the evil one. Take the helmet of salvation and the sword of the Spirit which is the word of God.

Oh to see the dawn
(The power of the cross)

Keith Getty
& Stuart Townend

With strength

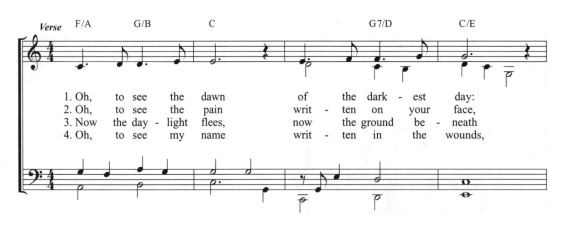

1. Oh, to see the dawn of the dark - est day:
2. Oh, to see the pain writ - ten on your face,
3. Now the day - light flees, now the ground be - neath
4. Oh, to see my name writ - ten in the wounds,

Christ on the road to Cal - va - ry. Tried by sin - ful
bear - ing the awe - some weight of sin. Ev - 'ry bit - ter
quakes as its Ma - ker bows his head. Cur - tain torn in
for through your suf - f'ring I am free. Death is crushed to

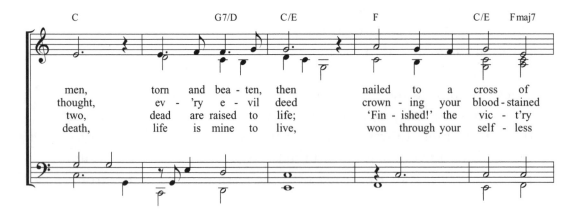

men, torn and bea - ten, then nailed to a cross of
thought, ev - 'ry e - vil deed crown - ing your blood - stained
two, dead are raised to life; 'Fin - ished!' the vic - t'ry
death, life is mine to live, won through your self - less

This song is recorded on the Spring Harvest New Songs 'Our God reigns' album.

68

One is the body

John L. Bell

1. One is the bo-dy and one is the Head, one is the
2. Christ who as-cen-ded to hea-ven a-bove is the same
3. Gifts have been gi-ven well-suit-ed to each; some to be
4. Called to his ser-vice are wo-men and men so that his

Spi-rit by whom we are led; one God and Fa-ther, one
Je-sus whose na-ture is love, who once de-scen-ded to
pro-phets to pas-tor or preach, some, through the gos-pel, to
bo-dy might e-ver a-gain wit-ness through wor-ship, through

faith and one call for all._____
bring to this earth new birth._____
chal-lenge, con-vert and teach._____
deed and through word to Christ our Lord.

Our God is an awesome God
(Awesome God)

Rich Mullins

70 Saviour, thank you for your love
(What a Saviour)

David Clifton, John Hartley
& Gary Sadler

1. Sa - viour, thank - you for your love, the love that gives me shel - ter from the storm. Held in your woun - ded hands, for - e - ver I will stand, safe be - neath the sha - dow of your cross.

2. Je - sus, Lord, you know my heart, let me be sur - ren - dered to your will. Though it costs e - v'ry - thing, I give it all to bring a life that is de - vo - ted to your way.

For bles - sed are the ones who seek you, bles - sed are the ones

This song works well in the key of B or B♭ for small groups.

This song is recorded on the Spring Harvest New Songs 'Our God reigns' album.

who trust you, bles - sed are the ones who fear your name.

Hal - le - lu - jah! Hal - le - lu -

- jah! What a Sa - viour,

hal - le - lu - jah!

-jah! Hal - le- -jah!

169

Search me, know me

Mildred Rainey & Kathryn Scott

Prayerfully ♩ = 84

Search me, know me, try me and see ev'ry worth-less af - fec - tion hid - den in me. All I'm ask - ing for is that you'd cleanse me, Lord.

Chorus

Cre-ate in me a heart that's clean, con-quer the pow'r
of right - eous - ness, co - ver my na -

This song is recorded on the Spring Harvest New Songs 'Our God reigns' album

72 See his love nailed to a cross

Tom Lockley

Rock style

1. See his love nailed_____ to a cross,___ per-fect and blame-less life___ gi-ven as sac-ri-fice.___ See him there all in the name of love,___ bro-ken, yet glo-ri-ous,___ all for the sake of us.___

2. Grea-ter love no one could e-ver show.___ Mer-cy so un-de-served,___ free-dom I should not know.___ All my sin, all of my hid-den shame___ died with him on the cross,___ e-ter-ni-ty won for us.___

Chorus

This is Je-sus in his glo-ry, King of hea-ven, dy-ing for me.

Bm | G | A | F♯

It is fi-nished, he has done—it. Death is bea-ten, hea-ven beck-ons

Bm | *(Fine)* Bm | A/C♯

me. Such love,— such love,—

F♯m | G *repeat x4* / *4th time D.S. al fine*

such love— is this— for me.—

72a In a battle

Sovereign God, we are in a battle, but you are Lord
We are in a battle for the truth, but you are Lord
We are in a battle for the Kingdom, but you are Lord
We are in a battle to shine as lights, but you are Lord
We are in a battle to be heard, but you are Lord
Sovereign God, we are in a battle, but you are Lord.

73

See, what a morning
(Resurrection hymn)

Victoriously

Stuart Townend
& Keith Getty

1. See, —— what a mor - ning, glo - rious - ly bright, with the
2. See —— Ma - ry weep - ing, 'Where is he laid?' As in
3. One —— with the Fa - ther, An - cient of Days, through the

dawn - ing of hope in Je - ru - sa - lem;
sor - row she turns from the emp - ty tomb;
Spi - rit who clothes faith with cer - tain - ty,

fold - ed the grave - clothes, tomb —— filled with light, as the
hears —— a voice speak - ing, call - ing her name; it's the
ho - nour and bles - sing, glo - ry and praise to the

an - gels an - nounce Christ is ris - en!
Ma - ster, the Lord raised to life a - gain!
King crowned with pow'r and au - tho - ri - ty!

This song is recorded on the Spring Harvest Live Worship 2004 album

See God's sal - va - tion— plan, wrought in love, borne in pain,— paid in
The voice that spans the— years, speak - ing life, stir - ring hope,— bring - ing
And we are raised with— him, death is dead, love has won,— Christ has

sa - cri - fice,_____ ful - filled in Christ, the— man, for he
peace_____ to us,_____ will sound till he ap - pears, for he
con - quered;_____ and we shall reign with— him, for he

lives: Christ is ri - sen from the dead!_____
lives, Christ is ri - sen from the dead!_____
lives, Christ is ri - sen from the dead!_____

74

Sing to the King
(Come let us sing a song)

Billy James Foote
1st verse and theme from 'Sing we the King'
by Charles Silvester Horne (1865-1914)

Joyfully ♩ = 108

Verse

1. Sing to the King who is com-ing to reign;
2. For his re-turn-ing we watch and we pray;

glo-ry to Je-sus, the Lamb that was slain. Life and sal-
we will be rea-dy the dawn of that day, we'll join in

va-tion his em-pire shall bring, and joy to the
sing-ing with all the re-deemed, 'cause Sa-tan is

na-tions, when Je-sus is King. Come, let us sing
van-quished and Je-sus is King.

Chorus

_ a song,— a song de-clar-ing that we__ be-long__ to Je - sus;

he is all__ we need. Lift up a heart_

_ of praise.__ Sing now with voi - ces raised__ to Je - sus;

sing to__ the King.

75

Take this moment,
sign and space

John L. Bell

(All)	1.	Take this mo-ment, sign and space, take my friends a-
(Men)	2.	Take the time to call my name, take the time to
(All)	3.	Take the tired-ness of my days, take my past re-
(Women)	4.	Take the lit-tle child in me, scared of grow-ing
(All)	5.	Take my tal-ents, take my skills, take what's yet to

round;_____ here a-mong us make the place
mend_____ who I am and what I've been,
gret,_____ let-ting your for-give-ness touch
old;_____ help me here to find my worth
be;_____ let my life be yours, and yet

where your love is found._____
all I've failed to tend._____
all I can't for-get._____
made in Christ's own mould._____
let it still be me._____

75a Today

Based on Psalm 95

Today, will you listen for his voice?
Do you want to hear?
How will you cope when he speaks?
Do you want to hear?
Today, if he speaks of love will you accept it?
If he speaks of truth will you believe it?
If he speaks of laying down, will you release it?
If he speaks of vision will you see it?
Are you ready now to worship, to kneel down?
Today, if you hear his voice –
Do not harden your hearts.

76

Thank you

Danny Cope

Capo 3(D)

Chorus

Thank you for your pa - tience and your end - less mer - cy,

thank you for the bless - ings you keep pour - ing on me.

Thank you for your gra - cious-ness and un - re - lent - ing faith -

4th time to Coda ⊕   *3rd time D.C. al Coda*

- ful - ness; thank you for mak - ing me.
(2.) tak - ing me.
(3.) sav - ing me.

(continued over...)

This song is recorded on the Spring Harvest New Songs 'Our God reigns' album

181

77

The Lord is One

Paul Field

1. The Lord is One,___ his heart is un-di-vi-ded,___
2. The Lord is One,___ the u-ni-ver-sal Sa-viour,___
3. The Lord is One,___ so we may come___ to-ge-ther,___
4. The Lord is One,___ the au-thor of cre-a-tion,___

through-out the years___ his faith-ful-ness___ un-changed.___ Through Christ, his
for east and west___ his word re-mains___the same.___ The one true
all hearts u-nite,___ all peo-ple live___ in peace.___ Sa-viour of
his migh-ty pow'r___ is mer-cy deep___and___ free.___ King of all

Son, the Fa-ther has___ pro-vi-ded___ light for the world___ to
God, the Prince of grace___ and fa-vour,___ born as a man___ to
all who con-quered death___ for-e-ver;___ e-ter-nal hope___ we
life, the God of ev-'ry na-tion;___ our com-mon ground___ his

shine for all___ man-kind.
die up-on___ a cross.
find in him___ a-lone.
love for all___ the world.

78

The rising sun that fills the sky
(Almighty God)

Tim Hughes

Capo 2(G)
Strong beat

1. The ri - sing sun that fills the sky, the star - ry host
2. The vast ex - panse of earth and sea, held by you

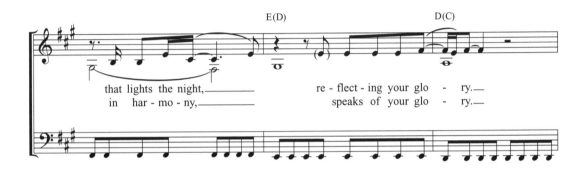

that lights the night,_____ re - flect - ing your glo - ry.___
in har - mo - ny,_____ speaks of your glo - ry.___

The moun - tain heights___ for - e - ver stand,___
All you've made___ since time be - gan,___

the rain that falls to soak the land_____ re - spond to your glo-
life it - self your per - fect plan;_____ and it's all for your glo-

(continued over...)

184

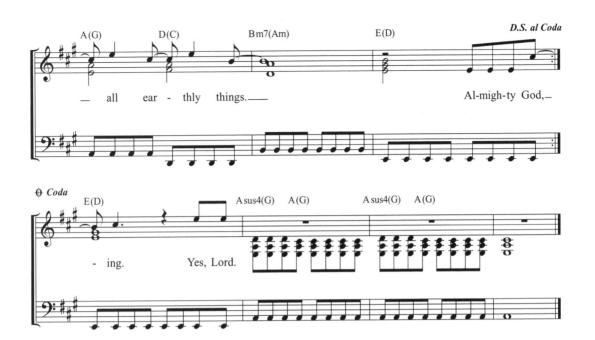

78a Sing for joy

From Psalm 95

Come, let us sing for joy to the Lord;
We will shout out loud to the rock of our salvation.
Let us come before him with thanksgiving
We will praise him with music and in song.
The Lord is the great God,
our great King is above all gods.
The deepest places of the earth are in his hands and the highest
mountains belong to him.
The sea is his, for he made it, and his hands formed the dry land.
Let us bow down in worship,
let us kneel before the Lord our Maker;
he is our God and we are under his care.
Let us sing for joy to the Lord.

The splendour of the King
(How great is our God)

Capo 3 (G)

Chris Tomlin, Jesse Reeves
& Ed Cash

This song is recorded on the Spring Harvest New Songs 'Sing' album

80

The winds are blowing
(Now is the time)

Delirious? & Matt Redman

1. The winds are blow-ing through a-gain, so we must fol-low. A peo-ple dar-ing to be-lieve we can change to-mor-row, and be the mi-ra-cle of light, and we won't give up the fight.

2. The ri-ver's run-ning through a-gain, re-ju-ve-nat-ing. For ev-'ry-thing you touch, you change, and we've all been chang-ing. We're a ci-ty shin-ing on a hill, tell this world you're shin-ing still,

Verse 2 only

tell this world you al-ways will.

Je - sus,— Je - sus, raise a church that's— shin - ing bright.

(Je - sus,— Je - sus.)

I want to fol - low, but what does it mean to
No - thing I own here is e - ver my own, when I
lay down my rights, see the world through your eyes and
I want to have you in all of my world so

(Je - sus,— Je - sus.)

live in this world and keep ev - 'ry - thing clean?
live in the mer - cy and bless - ing you've shown. I
fight for the hun - gry who pay for our lives.

(Je - sus,— Je -

Je - sus, con - sume me, flow

(Vocal 1st time only)

- sus.)

through me, cos now is the time (for us to shine.)

'Cos now is— the time for us to

shine, shine with the face of
Christ di - vine. No com - promise for all hea - ven cries 'now is the
time!'

81 There's a dance that all creation
(Dance of our God)

Capo 4 (Am)
With a reggae rhythm

Geraldine Latty & busbee

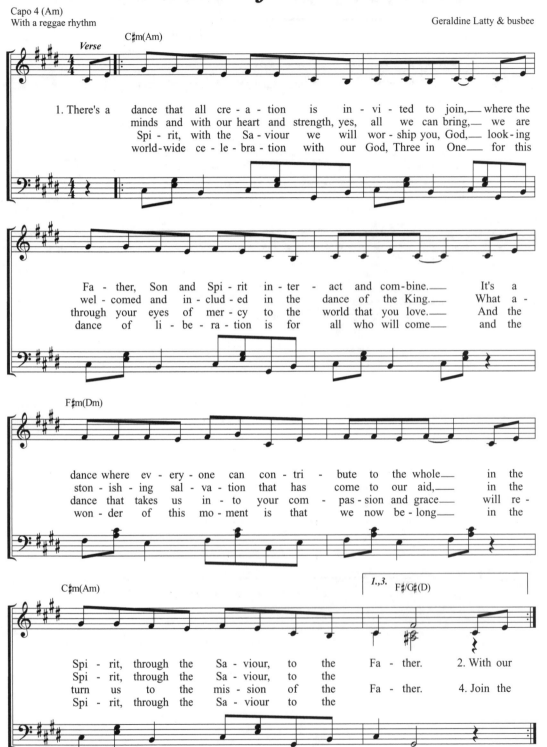

1. There's a dance that all cre-a-tion is in-vi-ted to join,— where the
minds and with our heart and strength, yes, all we can bring,— we are
Spi-rit, with the Sa-viour we will wor-ship you, God,— look-ing
world-wide ce-le-bra-tion with our God, Three in One— for this

Fa-ther, Son and Spi-rit in-ter-act and com-bine.— It's a
wel-comed and in-clud-ed in the dance of the King.— What a-
through your eyes of mer-cy to the world that you love.— And the
dance of li-be-ra-tion is for all who will come— and the

dance where ev-ery-one can con-tri-bute to the whole— in the
ston-ish-ing sal-va-tion that has come to our aid,— in the
dance that takes us in-to your com-pas-sion and grace— will re-
won-der of this mo-ment is that we now be-long— in the

1.,3. F#/G#(D)

Spi-rit, through the Sa-viour, to the Fa-ther. 2. With our
Spi-rit, through the Sa-viour, to the Fa-ther. 4. Join the
turn us to the mis-sion of the Fa-ther.
Spi-rit, through the Sa-viour to the

82

There is a green hill
in a far away country

Phil Baggaley, David Clifton
& Ian Blythe
Words adpt. from the hymn by C.F. Alexander

Steadily

1. There is a green hill in a far-a-way
2. I may not know of the pain of his
3. So ve-ry dear-ly Je-sus has

coun-try, it stands near a ci-ty, out-side a wall,
pas-sion, but I be-lieve that in my place he stood:
loved us, and all he would ask is that we love him too,

where Je-sus our Sa-viour, the King of all glo-ry
that I may know free-dom and live in for-give-ness,
and trust him for all that this life lays be-fore us,

suf - fered and died to save_____ us all.
for I am re - deemed by his_____ great love.
that we would try his work_____ to do.

Chorus There was no o - ther good e - nough, will-ing to pay the price of

sin. For he was the on - ly one who could reach out

and un - lock the gates of heav'n to let us in.

1st time D.C.
3rd time D.SS.
(Fine)
2nd time D.S.

195

There is a higher throne

83

Keith & Kristyn Getty

1. There is a high-er throne than all this world has known, where
2. And there we'll find our home, our life be-fore the throne; we'll

faith-ful ones from e-very tongue will one day come.
ho-nour him in per-fect song, where we be-long.

Be-fore the Son we'll stand, made fault-less through the Lamb; be-
He'll wipe each tear-stained eye, as thirst and hun-ger die; the

liev-ing hearts find pro-mised grace, sal-va-tion comes.
Lamb be-comes our Shep-herd King, we'll reign with him.

84

There is no other name

Steadily

Calvin Hollingworth

1. There is no o-ther name, for whom the an - gels dance\
   o - ther name, for whom e - ven the wind

_ a - round the throne, no o-ther name. There is no\
_ and waves are stilled, no o-ther name. There is no

o-ther name, for whom the an - gels rolled a - way the stone, no o-ther name.\
o-ther name, in whom our hearts can e - ver be ful-filled, no o-ther name.

(continued over...)

85

There's no condemnation
(I'm alive)

Simon Brading

Capo 2(A)
With energy

1. There's no con-dem-na-tion; in this sal-va-tion I'm free. Sin I was slave to, Sin now has no pow'r o-ver me.
2. Ob-jects of wrath, re-deemed at the cross from our sin. Cho-sen and liv-ing, for-e-ver for-gi-ven by him.
3. Je-sus, your blood will speak of your love for all time. Grace for to-day and hope for to-mor-row is mine.

I don't de-serve it, have not earned it, it's your grace on me, and now my heart is

(continued over...)

cel-e-bra-tion— of— your— grace,— cel-e-bra-tion of—

— your grace.— With a song— of love— and a shout— of— praise,—

cel-e-bra-tion. I'm a-live—

D.S. al Fine

85a Light of the world

Father God, who in the beginning brought order and light to
disorder and darkness, bring order again to your world.
Jesus, light of the world, where there is darkness of war, fear, grief or
sin; shine your light.
Spirit of the living Jesus, so live in our lives that we delight to be light
and life to those we meet and reflect your glory in all we do.
In the knowledge that one day we will live with you in your kingdom
of eternal light. **Amen.**

86

This is how I know what love is
(Extravagant, magnificent)

David Gate

With strength

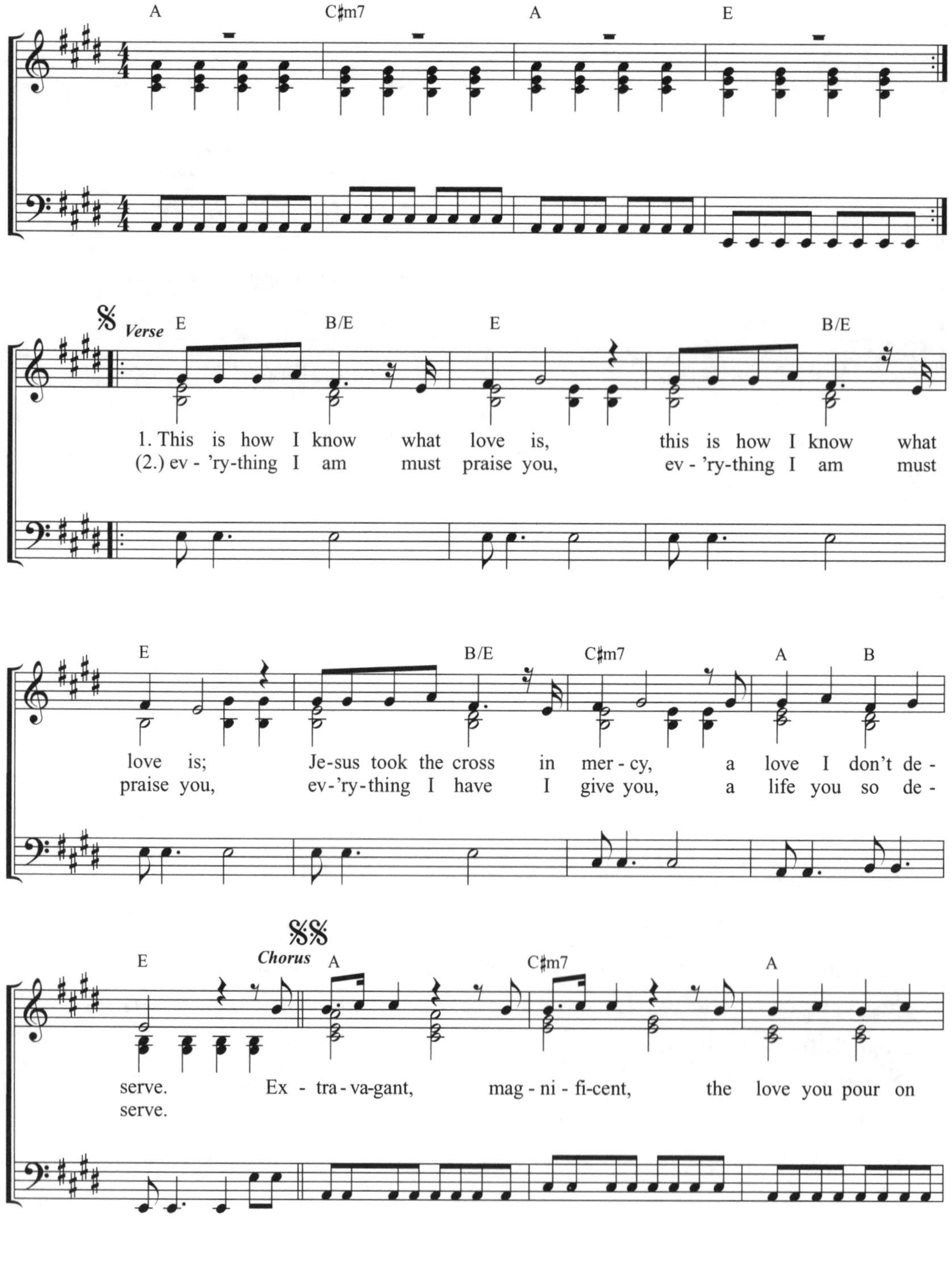

A C♯m7 A E
Verse E B/E E B/E
1. This is how I know what love is, this is how I know what
(2.) ev - 'ry-thing I am must praise you, ev - 'ry-thing I am must
E B/E C♯m7 A B
love is; Je-sus took the cross in mer - cy, a love I don't de -
praise you, ev-'ry-thing I have I give you, a life you so de -
E Chorus A C♯m7 A
serve. Ex - tra - va-gant, mag - ni - fi-cent, the love you pour on
serve.

me, ex - tra -va-gant, mag - ni -fi-cent,—— your grace I have re -

ceived. 2. Now

- ceived. Ex - - ceived.

This is how I know what love is, this is how I know what love is; it's

on - ly by the grace of Je - sus, it's on - ly by the grace of Je - sus. Ex -

205

This is our greatest joy
(Hallelujah)

Noel & Tricia Richards

1. This is our great-est joy: to know that we are yours.
2. You left your Fa-ther's home, in-to our world you came,
3. Your light of life has come, your Spi-rit makes us strong.

We live to wor-ship you, the Lord most high.
the In-no-cent who bore our guilt and shame.
Great hope for all the world through all you've done.

Ma-ker of this world, you formed us from the dust.
When you gave your life, the vic-to-ry was won:
We will wor-ship you, we will ap-plaud your ways;

Our lives will hon-our you, our voi-ces sing: Hal-
with thank-ful hearts we sing this song of praise:
in-to your pre-sence come with songs of praise:

le - lu-jah,— hal-le - lu - jah, we cry hal -

le - lu - jah.

87a Call to worship

Come now to worship the One: God of all time, all space, all people.
Come now to worship the One: God of our time, our space, our needs.
Come now to worship the One.

As we come to praise
You are God, you are One
As we come to celebrate
You are God, you are One
As we come to repent
You are God, you are One
As we go to follow
You are God, you are One

88

Though I walk
(You reign)

Simon Brading

209

89

Though trials will come
(Consider it joy)

Graham Kendrick

shap-ing us—— out of his love for us,—— mak-ing us
a-ny-thing,—— 'til we're com-plete in him,—— in ev-ery-thing

Chorus

more like Je-sus. Con-si-der it joy, pure joy——
more like Je-sus.

when trou-bles come. Ma-ny trials—— will make—— you strong.—— Con-si-der it

Last time to Coda

joy, pure joy—— and stand your—ground, then at last—you'll wear—

— a crown.——

(continued over...)

212

A rough guide to PsalmSurfing

PsalmSurfing is the name I give to the improvised singing of scripture – especially the Psalms. It works best where there is no other agenda but 'waiting on God'. It requires improvisational skills, faith and spiritual sensitivity, and for public settings the ability to create security and steer a wise course.

Why is it so special?
- Riding on 100% Word of God
- Responding to the inspiration of the moment
- Rest from the song list and respite from predictable patterns

What is it good for?
- Personal devotion
- Small group worship and prayer meetings
- Music Team/Choir rehearsals
- Going to scriptures songs rarely visit
- Creating a context where various art forms can respond to the inspiration of sung scripture

How to get started
- Practice in private or in your core music team
- Wait on God for direction
- Manage peoples' expectations – a short demonstration is helpful
- Assess the people and situation to pitch an appropriate level
- Choose a key and set the tempo. 'Imagine' the first line – sing it, or read until the words 'sing'
- Identify a 'refrain' that all could sing
- Give clear verbal cues i.e. 'listen', 'repeat', 'sing after me'
- Make space for reflection/silence/instrumental/poetry/art/dance
- Reinforce any emerging theme
- Take notes, evaluate and correct anything unhelpful

Lyrical versions of Scripture work the best. Scripture on screen is helpful, but a *Bible-in-hand* approach enables people to browse, and cross-reference.

What to look out for
- Avoid boring repetition; if you sing yourself into a 'dead end' just stop and start again!
- 'U.R.I.' (Unreal Religious Intensity!) and gratuitous improvisation
- Scripture taken out of context; the 'dark side' of the Psalms – knowing the Psalms and reading ahead is recommended!

Turn my face again
(Once for all)

90

Capo 5(C)

Martin Layzell

1. Turn my face again towards the cross
2. Kneel me down again before the cross
3. Lead me to the place your body lay,

on the mount of Cal-va-ry.
where they pierced your hands and feet.
where the stone lies rolled a-way.

Take me back again to pon-der on the life
King so hum-ble in a crown of thorns. The scars
Clothed in ma-je-sty and vic-to-ry, you rose

1st time only

— you gave, the price you paid to save me.
— you wear were mine to bear for-e-ver.
— a-gain and death is slain for-e-ver.

215

91

Turn your ear to heaven
(Oh praise him)

David Crowder

Capo 1 (A)
With praise

Verse Bb2(A2)   F/A(E/G#)

1. Turn your ear___ to hea-ven, and hear___ the noise___
2. Turn your gaze___ to hea-ven, and raise___ a joy-

Eb(D)   Bb2(A2)

- in-side,___ the sound___ of___ an- gels' awe,___ the sound___
- ous noise.___ The sound___ of sal-va- tion come,___ the sound___

F/A(E/G#)   Eb(D)

- of an-gels' songs, and all___ this for___ a King.___ We-
- of res- cued ones,___ and all___ this for___ a King. An-

Cm7(Bm7)   Eb(D)   *2nd time to chorus*

- could join___ and sing,___ all___ to Christ,___ the King.___
- gels join___ to sing,___ all___ for Christ___ the King.

𝄉 F/A(E/G#)   Eb(D)   F/A(E/G#)   Eb(D)

How con- stant, how___ di- vine,___ this song___ of ours___ will rise.___
How in- fi- nite___ and sweet,___ this love___ so res- cu- ing.___

This song is recorded on the Spring Harvest New Songs 'Our God reigns' album

Unapproachable light

David Gate

Un - ap - proach - a - ble light,___ so bright___ it is fright - 'ning, ho - li - ness shin - ing.
You're the pur - est of lights,___ can't see___ with - out dy - ing, there___ is no hid - ing.

Just glimp - ses___ we see___ to - day,___ but in hea - ven___ we'll see___ your face.___

Where no___ heart will___ de - ny___ the beau - ty___ of Christ___ seat - ed___ on high.___

And all___ tongues will___ pro-claim___ your worth and___ your fame,___ for e-ter-ni-ty___ to reign,___ there___ will on-ly be one name.___

93

We are a shining light
(Do something beautiful)

Graham Kendrick

1. We are a shin-ing light, ci-ty on a hill that can't be hid-den,
2. We are the salt of the earth, here to pu-ri-fy and fla-vour,

a shin-ing light. And this shin-ing light
salt of the earth. Sent through all the earth

is the life of Je-sus in us, oh what a light! The fire of his
to love God and love our neigh-bour, salt of the earth. As free-ly as

Spi - rit burns with jus-tice, joy and peace
we re-ceived so free-ly we must give,

and works through our hands and feet.
and we are his hands and feet.

Chorus

Go do something beautiful, in the name of Jesus

do something beautiful. Go do something Jesus would,

1.
do something beautiful, do something

beautiful. 2. do something beautiful.

(continued over...)

We come in your name
(You have been lifted)

94

With energy

Kate Simmonds
& Mark Edwards

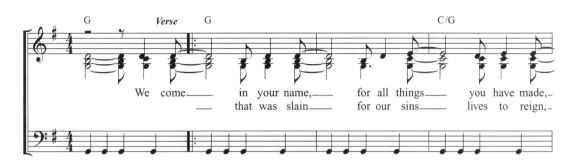

We come___ in your name,___ for all things___ you have made,___
___ that was slain___ for our sins___ lives to reign,___

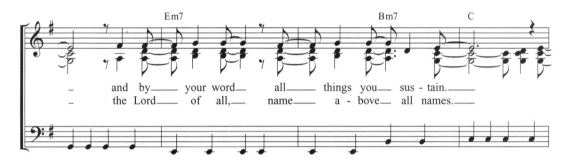

___ and by___ your word___ all___ things you___ sus - tain.___
___ the Lord___ of all,___ name___ a - bove___ all names.___

The Lamb___ We have___ been saved___ by faith___ in - to___ your glo-

rious name,___ and this___ a gift___ of grace,___ free - ly gi - ven us.___

(continued over...)

We come to be with you today

95

Gareth Robinson

Driving

Verse

1. We come to be with you today, our God.
come to-ge-ther as your peo-ple now.

We come to bring the praise that you de-serve.
We come u-ni-ted by the Sa-viour's blood.

Thanks-gi-ving, hands clap-ping,
Peace-mak-ing, hands serv-ing,

mouths sing-ing, liv-ing to wor-ship you with heart and soul and
mouths bless-ing, liv-ing by grace to love our neigh-bour as we

Chorus

mind and strength. Praise you, Lord, for all that you are.
love our-selves.

Praise you, Lord,— for all that— you've done.—

Praise you,— Lord,— for all that— you made us— to

Last time to Coda

be.— *1.* *2.*

2. We By

Bridge

grace we have— been saved through faith,— and

faith is your gift which we now re - ceive. *D.S. al Coda*

Coda

be.—

96

We stand and lift up our hands
(Holy is the Lord)

Chris Tomlin & Louie Giglio

With praise ♩ = 84

We stand and lift up our hands,___ for the joy___ of the Lord___ is our strength.

We bow down___ and wor - ship him now;___ how great,

___ how awe - some is he.___ And to-ge-ther we___ sing,___

e - v'ry - one___ sing:___ 'Ho-ly is___ the Lord___

This song is recorded on the Spring Harvest New Songs 'Our God reigns' album.

God___ Al - migh - ty;___ the earth___ is filled___ with his glo -

- ry. Ho - ly is___ the Lord___ God___ Al - migh - ty;___ the earth___

Last time to Coda

- ___ is filled___ with his glo - ry,___ the earth___ is filled___ with his glo -

1.

2.

- ry.'___ It is ris - ing up___ all___

- a-round; it's the an - them of___ the Lord's___ re-nown.___ It's ris -

(continued over...)

- ing up— all— a-round;— it's the an - them of— the Lord's—

— re-nown.— It is ris - — re-nown.— And to-ge-ther we— sing—

— ry, — the earth— is filled— with his glo - ry.'—

96a Prayer

It is right to give him thanks and praise.
Lord give us courage so that, without fear, we may call upon your
Holy Spirit and as we are gathered here in one place give us the grace
to know that you have heard us and are here with us, as you told us
through your Son Jesus Christ. **Amen.**

97 Welcomed in to the courts of the King
(Facedown)

Capo 5 (Am)

Matt & Beth Redman

Steadily, with reverence

1. Wel - comed in____ to the courts of the King,____ I've been
2. There is none____ in the hea - vens like you,____ and up -

u - shered in____ to your pre - sence.____ Lord, I stand____ on your
on the earth,____ who's your e - qual? You are far a - bove,____ you're the

mer - ci - ful ground,____ yet with e - v'ry step____ tread with
high - est of heights,____ I am bow - ing down____ to ex -

re - v'rence.____

(continued over...)

This song is recorded on the Spring Harvest New Songs 'Sing' album

232

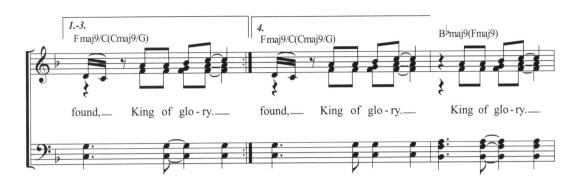

found,— King of glo-ry.— found,— King of glo-ry.— King of glo-ry.—

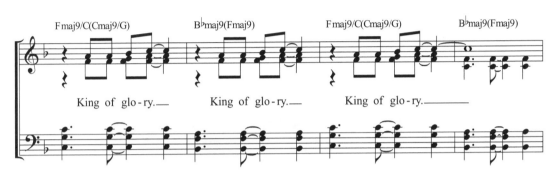

King of glo-ry.— King of glo-ry.— King of glo-ry.—

D.S.

And I'll

 Coda

98

When all around is fading
(Whole world in his hands)

Tim Hughes

1. When all a-round is fad - ing, and no-thing seems to last,
2. When I walk through fi - re, I will not be burned:

— when each day is filled with sor - row, still I
— when the waves come crash - ing round me, still I

know with all my heart: He's got the whole world in his hands,

he's got the whole world in his hands, I'll fear no e -

-vil, for you are with—— me, strong to de-li - ver, migh-ty to save.—

He's got the whole world in his hands.——

He's got the whole world in his hands.——

99

When all around I feel despair

Capo 4(G)
Rhythmically

Gareth Robinson

1. When all a-round I feel de-spair— and all my hope is gone, I
put my con-fi-dence in you,— you tell me I'm se-cure, and
great a gift that you should give— your Son that I'd go free. So

look to your e-ter-nal word,— find strength to car-ry on. Un-dy-ing words of
you'll pro-vide for all my needs,—through all that I en-dure. Your words of life re-
ev-er shall I praise your name,— for all e-ter-ni-ty. No sor-row, fear or

bound-less— grace so free-ly poured on me.— I trust in each and
store my— hope, a breath of clean fresh air,— so, stron-ger do I
e-vil— foe can steal your love a-way. Each day I hold on-

ev-'ry one and walk on grate-ful-ly.— 2. I
take each step and cast off all de-spair.— 3. How
to your word, your life, your word, your grace.

When I see the beauty
(What can I do)

Paul Baloche & Graham Kendrick

1. When I see the beau-ty of a sun-set's
sto-ry of a God of

glo-ry, a-maz-ing ar-tis-try a-cross the eve-ning
mer-cy who shared hu-ma-ni-ty and suf-fered by our

sky. When I feel the my-ste-ry of a dis-tant
side. Of the cross they nailed you to, that could not

ga-la-xy, it awes and hum-bles me to be
hold you, now you're mak-ing all things new, by the

(continued over...)

This song is recorded on the Spring Harvest New Songs 'Our God reigns' album

238

100a   Evening prayer

O Lord, support us all the day long of this troublous life, until the
shadows lengthen and the evening comes, the busy world is hushed,
the fever of life is over, and our work is done. Then Lord, in your
mercy, grant us safe lodging, a holy rest, and peace at the last,
through Jesus Christ our Lord. **Amen.**

John H Newman (1801-1890)

101 When I consider the awesome splendour
(When I consider)

Capo 3 (D)

Dave Bilbrough

♩ = 68

1. When I con-si-der the awe-some splen-dour
2. O Rock of A-ges, I'll sing your prais-es;
3. All my en-dea-vours, my earth-ly trea-sures,

and great-ness of my___ God, I'm filled with won-der
e-ter-nal is your___ throne. Why should you call___ me,
I lay be-fore you___ now. To you, my Mak-er,

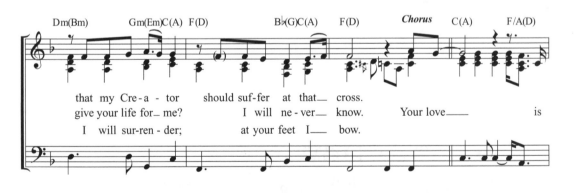

that my Cre-a-tor should suf-fer at that___ cross.
give your life for___ me? I will ne-ver___ know. Your love___ is
I will sur-ren-der; at your feet I___ bow.

Chorus

high-er than the hea-vens; your love___ is deep-er than the sea, your love___

102 When I look at the blood

Godfrey Birtill

When I__ look at the__ blood, all I see is love, love,
love. When I__ stop at the__ cross, I can see the love of
God.

But I can't see com-pe-ti - tion, I can't see hi-er-ar-
But I can't see un-for-give - ness, I can't see hate or en-

chy. I can't see pride or pre-ju-dice,__ or the a-buse of au-tho-
vy. I can't see stu-pid fight - ing,__ or__ bit-ter-ness or jea-

ri-ty. I can't see lust for po - wer, I can't see ma-ni-pu-la-
lou-sy. I can't see em-pire build - ing, I can't see self - im-por-

G D 1. G D.C.
tion. I can't see rage or an-ger or sel-fish am-bi-tion. When I
tance. I can't see back stab-bing or va-ni-ty or ar-
2. G D.C. al Coda
Coda
C 3
-ro-gance. When I And I see sur-ren-der, sa-cri-
G D G C
fice, sal-va-tion, hu-mi-li-ty. Right-eous-ness,
G D G G
faith-ful-ness, grace, for-give-ness. Love, love,
Repeat ad lib
Last time
Build . . .
D Em D C
love, love, love, love, love, love, love. Love, love, love. Love, love,
D G D/F# Em Rit . . . . D
love, when I stop at the cross, I can see the love of God.

Where, oh where's your presence O God

Godfrey & Gill Birtill,
Geraldine Latty & Tim Lomax

Steady 4

1. Where, oh where's your pre-sence, O God,— in this dry and wea-ry land?_____ So ma-ny peo-ple drift-ing a-way;— how we need to un-der-stand_____ you're still God, e-ven when___ we're un-be-liev-ing, still___ God, when we're

2. Where, oh where's your king-dom, O God?— We have let ho-li-ness go.___ So ma-ny i-dols lit-ter our land.— We've got to let this na-tion know_____ you're still God, when the go-vern-ment have— no an-swers, still___ God, when the

3. When will Je-sus real-ly be seen— through the church that bears his name?_____ A-gents of his king-dom, his peace,— in the world for which he came,_____ you're still God. E-ven though___ you were— re-jec-ted, still___ God. Though you

104

When I turn my eyes to see
(Lift my eyes – Psalm 121)

Steve James

Moderately

1. When I turn my eyes to see what the world can of - fer me, who a - lone can be my help? O lift my eyes from the fears that threat - en me and vain hopes to set me free, who a -

worlds are in his hands, the e - ver - more his king - dom stands, yet he keeps me in his gaze; O lift my eyes. He who wat - ches will not sleep for the Shep - herd guards his sheep, none can

247

heat of— the day. No e - vil— pre-vails in his pur - pose— for me, till his

D.S. al fine

face I see.———————— Lift my

104a We are thankful

There's a universe you made with stars and planets
You are the Creator, and we are thankful.
There's a world of land and sea and sky
You are the Creator, and we are thankful.
There are nations and tribes, clans and families
You are the Creator, and we are thankful.
There is the body of Christ, and we have a role
You are the Creator, and we are thankful.
There are gifts and abilities that you have given us
You are the Creator, and we are thankful.
There are people we're called to serve, young and old
You are the Creator, and we are thankful.
There is everything you made, and that includes me!
You are the Creator, and we are thankful.

Who is moving on the waters
(He is Yahweh)

105

With strength

Dean Salyn

Verse

D   Gsus2

1. Who is mov - ing on___ the wa - ters,___
2. Who is he that makes___ me hap - py,___

D   A

who is hold - ing up___ the moon,___
who is he that gives___ me peace,___

D   Gsus2

who is peel - ing back___ the dark - ness___
who is he that brings___ me com - fort,___

Bm7   Asus4   A

with the burn - ing light___ of___ noon?
and turns the bit - ter in - to___ sweet?

(continued over...)

106

Who can know?
(I stand in awe)

Martyn Layzell

With quiet intensity

1. Who can know the mind of our Cre-a-tor,
2. Who has weighed the dust of ev-'ry moun-tain,
3. You have seen the end from the be-gin-ning,

who can speak of won-ders yet un-seen;
who has walked the my-st'ries of the deep;
you have been be-fore the world be-gan;

who can reach the height of un-der-stand-ing, to
who has laid the earth on its foun-da-tion, and
you have reached to me with-in my dark-ness, and

play the notes of wis-dom's me-lo-dy?

Who is like you, Lord of heaven
(Great Redeemer)

Capo 3 (D)

Neil Bennetts
(Chorus words from Charles Wesley)

1. Who is like you, Lord of heaven, King of glory, 'throned in majesty? You are holy, you are holy.
2. Who can fathom all the riches of your mercy, of your faithfulness? You are worthy, you are worthy.

Chorus

O for a thousand tongues to sing my great Redeemer's praise, the honours of his name.

A - wake, my soul, and cel - le - brate___ the won-

- ders of___ his___ grace, let heav'n___ and earth___ join in___ the song.___

Last time

To continue

For you are ho - ly, you are ho -

Repeat 4 times then D.S.

- ly.___

108
Why so downcast, O my soul?
(Psalm 42)

Sam Hargreaves

Steadily

Why so down-cast,___ O my soul?

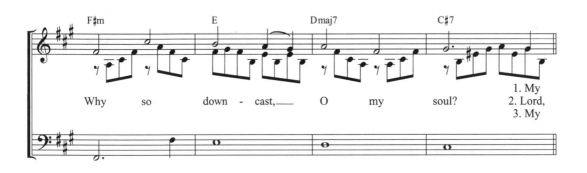

Why so down-cast,___ O my soul?

1. My
2. Lord,
3. My

food   has been tears,   my soul   thirsts for   you.
can   you for - get   the ones   that you   love?
hope   is   in   you,   my God   and my   Rock.

1.2.

Where can I   go and meet with God?
Where can I   go and meet with God?

3.

By day your

love di - rects me, at night your song is with me; an-swer my

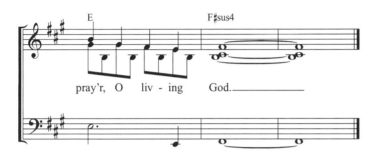

pray'r, O liv - ing God._____

108a   Cry for help

Based on Psalm 46

Our world is shaking
Desolation
Lost hope

The bewildered cry for help
But the strength of man is helpless

My eyes turn to you my comforter, deliverer
My everlasting hope

Where can they go to find mercy?
Who has compassion to cover the world?
Who hears the heart cry of nations?
Who knows the sorrow of souls?

My God, my refuge and strength
I cannot understand but I can trust
I can trust in you.

109

Wonderful you are
(Superlatives)

Mark Beswick & Howard Francis

Building with each verse

1. Won - der-ful, you are won - der-ful, you are won - der-ful.
2. Mar - vel-lous, you are mar - vel-lous, you are mar - vel-lous.
3. Glo - ri - ous, you are glo - ri - ous, you are glo - ri - ous.
4. Beau - ti - ful, you are beau - ti - ful, you are beau - ti - ful.

5. Ex - cel - lent, you are ex - cel - lent, you are
6. Prince of peace, you are Prince of peace, you are

ex - cel - lent.
Prince of peace.

7. Lord of all, you are
8. King of kings, you are

Lord of all, you are Lord of all.
King of kings, you are King of kings.

9. Migh-ty God,—you are migh-ty God,—you are migh-ty God.—

109a God our Creator

From Genesis 1:1–28

In the beginning, God created the heavens and the earth.
In the empty void and crushing darkness, God spoke light into being.
Creator God, bring light into our darkness.

In the beginning, God took eternity and formed time and space,
seasons, days and years.
Creator God, fill and shape the time you have given us.

In the beginning, God took land and sea and filled them with life of
every kind.
Creator God, help us find our place within your diverse creation.

In the beginning, God spoke his very image, and the returning echo
formed humanity.
**Creator God, open our eyes to see you reflected in every human
face.**

In the beginning, God created,
and it was good.

Copyright © 2006 Mark Earey

110 Worship God with the morning sunrise
(Worship God)

Capo 1(D)

Geraldine Latty & busbee

(continued over...)

We have come to give you praise, we have come to bless your name.

D.S. al Coda

We will al-ways be a-mazed at how you love. Wor-ship

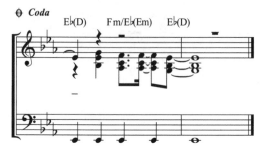

110a   One great God

We thank you that you are truth, and you are God for all
One huge God, One great God,
One amazing, holy God.
We thank you that you are sovereign, but you became human
One huge God, One great God,
One amazing, holy God.
We thank you that you are powerful, and you will be our strength
One huge God, One great God,
One amazing, holy God.

111

You are holy
(Prince of peace)

Mark Imboden & Tammi Rhoton

(continued over...)

fore _____ him.

_deem - er __ and __ Friend._ You're my Prince of __ peace and I will live my __ life for

you.   You are   you.

You're my Prince of __ peace and I will live my __ life for you.

112
You are more beautiful
(No one like you)

Jack Parker, Jason Solley, Jeremy Bush,
Mike Dodson, Mike Hogan & David Crowder

This song is recorded on the Spring Harvest iScape 'No one like you' album

267

113

You are the shout
of the nations

David Gate

1. You are the shout of the na - tions, you are the an-gels' song,
2. You are the source of all good things, you are the au-thor of life,

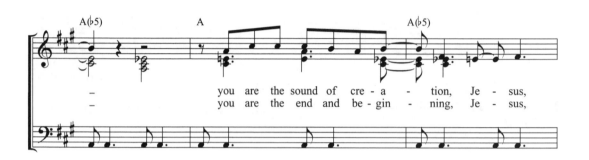

you are the sound of cre - a - tion, Je - sus,
you are the end and be - gin - ning, Je - sus,

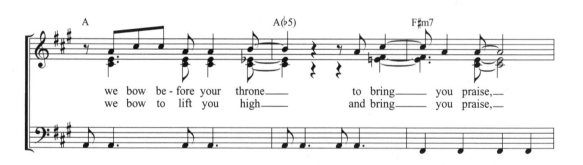

we bow be - fore your throne to bring you praise,
we bow to lift you high and bring you praise,

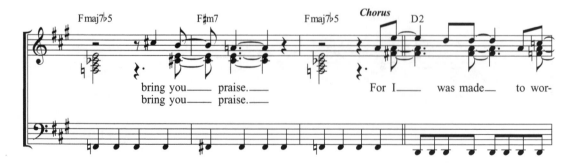

bring you praise. For I was made to wor-
bring you praise.

You chose the cross
(Lost in wonder)

Capo 3(G)

Martyn Layzell

Steadily

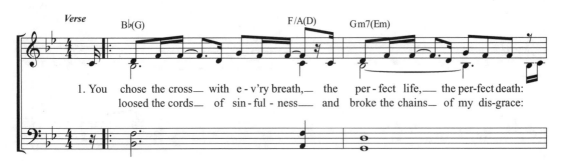

1. You chose the cross— with e-v'ry breath,— the per-fect life,— the per-fect death:
   loosed the cords— of sin-ful-ness— and broke the chains— of my dis-grace:

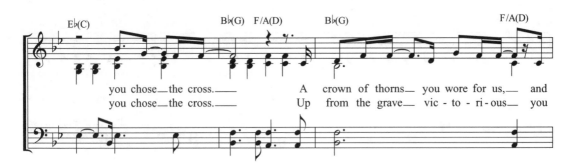

you chose— the cross.— A crown of thorns— you wore for us,— and
you chose— the cross.— Up from the grave— vic-to-ri-ous— you

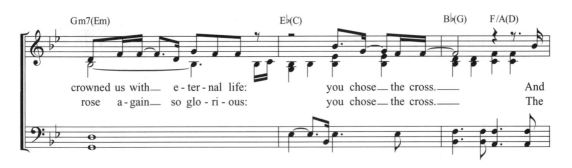

crowned us with— e-ter-nal life: you chose— the cross.— And
rose a-gain— so glo-ri-ous: you chose— the cross.— The

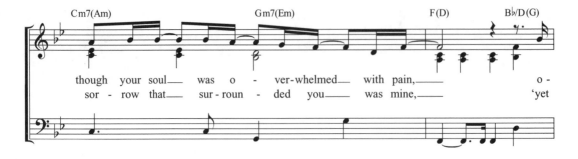

though your soul— was o-ver-whelmed— with pain,— o-
sor-row that— sur-roun-ded you— was mine,— 'yet

This song is recorded on the Spring Harvest New Songs 2003 album

be - di - ent____ to death____ you o - ver - came. I'm lost in
not my will____ but yours____ be done'____ you____ said.

won - der,____ I'm lost in____ love, I'm lost in praise for - e - ver more.____

_____ Be - cause of Je - sus'____ un - fail - ing____ love, I am for -

gi - ven,____ I am re - stored.____

(2. You)

115
You lived, you died
(All the earth will sing your praises)

Capo 3 (D)

Paul Baloche

You hear, O Lord

Graham Kendrick

fend - ing the fa - ther - less, and the op - pressed,

that they may live in fear no more. A -

rise, Lord!_____ Lift up your hand,_____

God of mer - cy save the help - less,

show your kind - ness. A - rise, O Lord!

(continued over...)

117 You stepped down from heaven's glory
(Let the world see Jesus)

Matt Hooper

1. You stepped down from hea-ven's glory, hum-bly came to earth.
2. Now this world you died for is the world I want to reach.

Sa-cri-ficed your-self for me and gave
And this love you gave us is the Fa-

— me grace and life its worth. You were lift-ed up so that peo-
— ther's love that lives in me.

— ple would be-lieve. Let the world see Je-sus Christ in me.

(continued over...)

(118) Your blood speaks a better word
(Nothing but the blood)

Matt Redman
Chorus inspiration: Nothing but the blood
by Robert Lowry (1876-1899)

1. Your blood speaks a bet-ter word____ than all the emp-ty claims__
(2.) cross te-sti-fies__ in grace,____ tells of the Fa-ther's heart__

__ I've heard up-on__ this earth;____ speaks right-eous-ness__ for me__
__ to make a way__ for us;____ now bold-ly we__ ap-proach,__

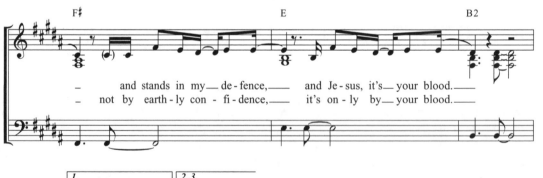

__ and stands in my__ de-fence,____ and Je-sus, it's__ your blood.__
__ not by earth-ly con-fi-dence,____ it's on-ly by__ your blood.__

1. Your   What can wash__ a-way____ our sins?__
What can wash__ us pure____ as snow?__

This song is recorded on the Spring Harvest Live Worship 2005 album and the Spring Harvest New Songs 'Sing' album

What can make us whole a-gain? No-thing but the blood,
Wel-comed as the friends of God? No-thing but your blood,

no-thing but the blood of Je - sus. Je - sus.
no-thing but your blood King

2. Your Je - sus.

Your mercy overwhelms me
(You're good Lord)

Capo 3(D)

Kathryn Scott

1. Your mer - cy o - ver - whelms___ me, more a - maz - ing ev - 'ry day;___ this kind___ ness straight___ from hea - ven is re - lent - less like___ the waves.___

cy o - ver - takes___ me, e - ven when___ my feet___ have strayed;___ and though___ I don't___ de - serve___ it, you sur - round___ me with___ your grace..

1. Your mer ___

You're good, Lord,

119a Help us give to you

Our provider God, who gives us so much,
help us to give to you.
Help us to give you our love every day
help us to give you our time to pray.
Help us to give you our work in serving
help us to give you our hearts by sharing.
Help us to give you our everything.
Our provider God, who gives us so much,
help us to give to you. **Amen.**

120 Your mercy taught us how to dance
(Dancing generation)

Matt Redman

With energy

Verse

mer - cy taught us how to dance,___ to ce - le - brate with
glo - ry taught us how to shout,___ we'll lift your name in

all we have,___ and we'll dance to___ thank you for mer - cy.
all the earth,___ and we'll shout to the praise of your glo - ry.

1.,3.   *2.,4.*   ***Bridge***

Your   It's the o - ver-flow   of a for -

gi - ven soul,   and now we've seen you, God,   our hearts___

Guitar Chords

Introduction

A good chord vocabulary is essential for a guitarist to feel confident when playing in worship, especially when the situation may involve reading a previously unseen piece of music or picking up a song quickly by ear. The chords on these pages are arranged in 'families' according to key. This is a beneficial way of remembering chords as most songs stick to these groupings. For each key, the first row shows the simplest form of each chord and the second line gives a more interesting substitution. The third line shows the chords most commonly used by guitarists derived by keeping some sort of pedal tone ringing in each chord and the fourth line shows inverted chords with an alternate bass note.

Also included are the Roman Numerals and Nashville Numbers associated with each chord. If you've not come across these before, they are simply an easy way of numbering each chord within a key. This is useful as it means you can take any chord progression in one key and instantly transpose it to another. Furthermore you can try out any of the chords in each column that corresponds to the relevant Roman Numeral and see if there is chord type or inversion which still fits but adds a different flavour. Experimentation like this may open up creative chord progressions that serve as a catalyst to help you to worship in fresh ways or to write new songs.

Please see the CD-ROM section of Spring Harvest Distinctive Sounds – More than a Song album and the Academy of Music Ministry's website at www.nexustrust.co.uk for details of more material relating to developing these skills.

	Roman	I	II	III	IV	V	VI	VII
	Nashville	1	2	3	4	5	6	7
Key of C	3-note chord (triad)	C	Dm	Em	F	G	Am	Bdim
Key of C	4-note chord	C maj7	Dm7	Em7	F maj7	G7	Am7	Bm7♭5
Key of C	Alternative substitute	C	D7sus4	Em7	F sus2	G5	Am7	Dsus4/B
Key of C	Alternative bass note	C/E	Dm/F	Em/G	F/A	F/G	Am/E	

For all chords in the key of C# or Db, use the chords from the key of C with capo 1

Guitar Chords

	Roman	I	II	III	IV	V	VI	VII
	Nashville	1	2	3	4	5	6	7
Key of D	3-note chord (triad)	D	Em	F#m	G	A	Bm	C#dim
	4-note chord	D maj7	Em7	F#m7	G maj7	A7	Bm7	C#m7♭5
	Alternative substitute	D sus2	Em9	F#m7	G6sus2	A7sus4	Bm11	Aadd9/C#
	Alternative bass note	D/F#	Em/B	F#m/A	G/B	G/A	Bm/F#	

For all chords in the key of D# or E♭, use the chords from the key of D with capo 1

		I	II	III	IV	V	VI	VII
Key of E	3-note chord (triad)	E	F#m	G#m	A	B	C#m	D#dim
	4-note chord	E maj7	F#m7	G#m7	A maj7	B7	C#m7	D#m7♭5
	Alternative substitute	E5	F#m11	G#madd♭6	Aadd9	Badd4	C#m7	D#alt
	Alternative bass note	E/G#	F#m/C#	G#m/D#	A/C#	A/B	C#m/G#	

For all chords in the key of F, use the chords from the key of E with capo 1

For all chords in the key of F# or Gb, use the chords from the key of E with capo 2

287

Guitar Chords

Roman	I	II	III	IV	V	VI	VII
Nashville	1	2	3	4	5	6	7

Key of G

	I	II	III	IV	V	VI	VII
3-note chord (triad)	G	Am	Bm	C	D	Em	F#dim
4-note chord	Gmaj7	Am7	Bm7	Cmaj7	D7	Em7	F#m7♭5
Alternative substitute	G	A7sus4	Dsus4/B	Cadd9	Dsus4	Em7	G/F#
Alternative bass note	G/D	Am/C	Bm/D	C/G	C/D	Em/G	

For all chords in the key of G# or A♭, use the chords from the key of G with capo 1

Key of A

	I	II	III	IV	V	VI	VII
3-note chord (Triad)	A	Bm	C#m	D	E	F#m	G#dim
4-note chord	Amaj7	Bm7	C#m7	Dmaj7	E7	F#m7	G#m7♭5
Alternative substitute	Asus2	Bsus4	C#m7	D6sus2	Eadd9	F#m11	Eadd9/G#
Alternative bass note	A/E	Bm/F#	C#m/E	D/A	D/E	F#m/A	

For all chords in the key of A# or Bb, use the chords from the key of A with capo 1

For all chords in the key of B, use the chords from the key of A with capo 2

Richard Stephenson & Andy Flannagan

Scripture Index

Scripture Index cont'd

Hebrews cont'd

James

1 Peter

Revelation

Spoken Worship Index

Thematic Index

Thematic Index cont'd